Moderate Drinking

Success Stories and Lessons Learned

TALES FROM THE MM COMMUNITY AND BEYOND

Edited by Mary K. Reid

Dedication

A fine glass vase goes from treasure to trash, the moment it is broken.
Fortunately, something else happens to you and me.
Pick up your pieces. Then, help me gather mine.

-Vera Nazarian, The Perpetual Calendar of Inspiration

Table of Contents

GLOSSARY

Abstinence (Abs): Refraining completely from drinking alcoholic beverages.

Abstar: MM sponsored online drink tracker

Alcohol Free (AF): Containing no alcohol.

Blue Day: Reference to the Abstar drink counter meaning a day in which the participant stayed within moderate drinking limits. (The numbers are displayed in blue.)

By the Book (BTB): Adhering to the Moderation Management limits of alcohol intake. (See Appendix A–Steps of Change).

F'abs: Abstaining from alcohol for four days in a week.

Gold Day: Reference to the Abstar drink counter meaning the participant abstained but also took another positive action toward health and long-term change.

Green Day: Reference to the Abstar drink counter meaning a day in which the participant abstained contentedly. (The numbers are displayed in green.)

MM Forum: Private online message board community for MM members.

High Five: Abstaining from alcohol for five days in a week.

Listserv: MM private community in which members communicate through email which is divided by subject threads. Also referred to as the Mainlist.

MM: Moderation Management, a peer-support community for people desiring to reduce their drinking.

Moderating: Adhering to a planned reduction of alcohol

Non-alcoholic: Containing no alcohol. Abbrev: NA

Moderation: Drinking within the recommended guidelines of   MM.

Onesie: Can refer to drinking only one drink in a day or abstaining for only one day. Also refers to a set of tools that can be applied one day at a time. (See Appendix B).

Red Day: Reference to the Abstar drink counter meaning the participant drank over moderate limits.

Roster: A list of members committing to an action for a day or week.

Sticky: A daily roster members "sign up" for if they intend to abstain from drinking that day.

Surfing: Waiting out the urge to drink.

The "30": A 30-day period of abstinence.

Trigger: An event or situation that increases the urge to drink.

Trike: Abstaining from alcohol for three days in a week.

WTF: Total loss of control as in, "What the "f..." happened?

INTRODUCTION

"Be moderate in order to taste the joys of life in abundance."
— Epicurus

What is Moderation Management? Does it really work? Where are the success stories? These are common questions we encounter at MM. We hope that this book and the members' stories it contains will answer these questions in a convincing enough manner to encourage any reader who desires to change their drinking habit or routine, in any way, to pursue those changes. We support you in the choice that is right for you.

From the Moderation Management Website (http://moderation.org/):

Moderation Management (MM) is a behavioral change program and national support group network for people

*concerned about their drinking who desire to make positive
lifestyle changes. MM empowers individuals to accept personal
responsibility for choosing and maintaining their own path,
whether moderation or abstinence. It promotes early self-
recognition of risky drinking behavior, when moderate drinking
is a more easily achievable goal. MM is run by lay members
who came to the organization to resolve personal issues and
stayed to help others.*

*MM was the first moderation-based support and help entry on
the the National Institute on Alcohol Abuse and Alcoholism
(NIAAA) "Rethinking Drinking" website under Info and Help
links: (https://www.rethinkingdrinking.niaaa.nih.gov/Help-
links/Default.aspx)*

THE VALUES THAT GUIDE MM:

- Members take personal responsibility for their own recovery from a drinking problem.
- People helping people is the strength of the organization.
- People who help others to recover also help themselves.
- Self-esteem and self-management are essential to recovery.

- Members treat each other with respect and dignity.

ASSUMPTIONS OF MM:

- Problem drinkers should be offered a choice of behavioral change goals.
- Harmful drinking habits should be addressed at a very early stage, before problems become severe.
- Problem drinkers can make informed choices about moderation or abstinence goals based upon educational information and the experiences shared at self-help groups.
- Harm reduction is a worthwhile goal, especially when the total elimination of harm or risk is not a realistic option.
- People should not be forced to change in ways they do not choose willingly.
- Moderation is a natural part of the process from harmful drinking, whether moderation or abstinence becomes the final goal. Most individuals who are able to maintain total abstinence first attempted to reduce their drinking, unsuccessfully. Moderation programs shorten the process of "discovering" if moderation is a workable solution

by providing concrete guidelines about the limits of moderate alcohol consumption.

Ready to get started?

◆ ◆ ◆

The members' stories included in this book have been submitted by actual MM members or people for whom MM has played a role in their journey toward a resolution of their drinking problems. The beliefs and ideas expressed are those of the individual writer. While MM supports each member in their individual beliefs and ideas, the ideas and beliefs expressed are not necessarily the beliefs and ideas of MM as an organization.

CHAPTER 1: BEGINNINGS

I f you've bought this book, you are at a new beginning. Whether this is your first and only contact with Moderation Management (MM) or whether you've been a member of MM for years, the stories in this book will take you down undiscovered paths which their authors have walked on their moderation journeys. They will inspire you to start your own journey or give you courage to explore a path different than the one with which you've grown familiar.

Courage to change. To grow. To begin. Or, begin again.

The stories you will read in the following chapters do not have endings, there will still be twists and turns to come, but the writers of those stories felt changed enough by their journeys with MM to share them as offers of encouragement to those who read them. They are written testimonies that things do get better, that there is hope, that, if they can change, so can you-no matter how bleak or lost or insurmountable the road looks from where you're standing right now.

Beginnings are scary. Beginnings aren't always given the sense of pride they deserve. But, every success story in the following chapters had a beginning story, a first cry for help or a desperate plea for a glimmer of hope. Every powerful word came from a down to the last drop of will to not give up.

Following, are the Beginning Stories of MM's members. They are compilations of first-time posts in the "New to MM? Start Here" thread on the MM Forum. They are based on real posts, but at MM, we remember how vulnerable we all felt as we wrote our first posts and we respect that our "Beginning Story" may not be the story we want to share with the world. Some of us typed out our first post with shaking hands and pushed "send" before we could change our minds. Some of us did it with excitement that, finally, we had found a community that "got us." And, yes, some of us did it hungover with a glass of "hair of the dog" at our elbow. Our Beginning Stories may differ in levels of fear, grit, enthusiasm and despair in their telling, but the one element that is present in every line of every story is hope. Because, without hope, the beginning cannot be written.

STORIES:

New And Feeling Alone

For years I've been struggling to cut down on my drinking without long-term success. It has been a lonely endeavor because I've been too embarrassed and ashamed to admit to anyone that I have a problem. So, I've been attempting to deal with my drinking on my own.

Mostly, I drink at home by myself so I've been able to hide how much and how often I drink. That's fine for day to day functioning in the world, but not so good for reaching out for help and support. My friends and family think I've got my act together and have a great life – and in many ways that is true – so why am I having so much trouble controlling my drinking?

A few months ago I was feeling stressed and began drinking even more than usual and reached out to a counselor who had experience treating addiction issues. It felt great to voice my concerns to another human being, but he was clearly skeptical that anyone with a drinking problem should do anything other than permanently abstain. He did, however, mention that there were moderate drinking groups on the internet, so I went looking.

I found MM a few weeks ago and it was such a revelation and comfort. I had no idea that there are so many out there who share in this struggle. I'm blown away by the compassion and understanding expressed in the posts. So much so that I'm leaving lurkdom, closing my eyes, taking a deep breath and jumping in.

Is Complete Abstinence Right For Me?

Hi. I'm Carl and this is my first post. I've been sober for the last 4 months after drinking daily for many years. I joined AA and have attended meetings every day during these 4 months. For the first month or so, I was convinced it was where I needed to be. The interaction in AA helped me recognize that alcohol has had a negative impact on my life and in my relationships, especially with my spouse. She feels I've been ignoring her and have been extremely critical of her after drinking too much. I'm working hard on this issue and we both feel that I've improved dramatically.

Step 1 of AA is admitting I am powerless over alcohol. While I realize that my drinking was excessive and physically and emotionally unhealthy, I don't truly feel that I am powerless. I'm not sure that I am physically addicted either and, while I recognize that I very well might be, I'm curious to find out if I really am. I googled "alternatives to AA" and found Moderation Management's website. MM seems like the perfect program to determine exactly where I stand so that I can move on with my life one way or another. I'm interested in resuming social drinking and having a cocktail in work situations, in a moderate fashion. If I prove to myself that I can't drink moderately, using the tools provided in this program, I'll go back to abstinence with a great deal more confidence.

I'm interested in any others who might have a similar experience of having been at one time convinced that abstinence was right for them and then successfully moved to a plan of moderation.

Anesthetized By Alcohol

Hello Everyone,

Like all of you I am here because I have a problem and am looking for a community that can support me in my efforts to moderate. For too long I have anesthetized myself with alcohol and felt the consequences but have done nothing to solve the problem. I had a score of 13 on the alcohol dependence questionnaire (http://moderation.org/newmembers/questionnaire.html) on the MM website, which indicates low/medium dependence. However, it is the gradual erosion of confidence, self-esteem, professional productivity, and loss of relationships that are more concerning to me. Also, the sheer amount of time and money spent on drinking over the years is staggering for me to think of. Therefore, I am here to explore whether moderation or abstinence is right for me.

I've read many insightful posts by members of this forum. Some echoed what I feel, and some made me think of my drinking in ways that I had not thought before. All were inspiring, especially the supportive responses written to help a member who was struggling. There is a great deal of honesty, humor, and candor here. I'm praying to find the hope, faith, and courage to begin this difficult journey with you all.

New Mom Seeking Support

I got pregnant last year so had to give up my partying and heavy alcohol use. I am now a mommy to a wonderful 10-month-old son. Being sober and pregnant and then while nursing added up to over a year of abstinence. After nursing, I began easing back into drinking wine with dinner every now and then. Within the past couple months, I've had several major blow-outs where my wine drinking started early during the day and went on into the night. I'm not my normal loving self when I've been drinking so much and I'm afraid it may be affecting my mothering ability. I don't want to become that mom who can't be there for my son because I'm drunk or hungover! I definitely need to either go back to sobriety or get support and tools to keep my drinking in check.

Age 25 And Seeking Answers

Hi everyone. I've been in a treatment center for about 6 weeks and have been "clean" now for 81 total days. I slowly realized I did not quite believe in everything they were trying to sell me at treatment and at AA. For example, I do not believe I am powerless, I do not believe I have a "disease" that talks to me and I do not believe that only jails, institutions and death are waiting for me at the end of a bottle.

I admit that I was drinking every night to fall asleep, only to wake up feeling unrested in the morning. Along with using alcohol as a sleep medication, I admit that I enjoy getting the buzz from drinking a bit too much. However, I never reached for a bottle in the morning and have no problem pacing my drinking or stopping after one. I also have never gotten into relationship or legal trouble.

I know I am capable of change and don't want to label myself an alcoholic at such a young age. I'm looking forward to proving myself right and showing my family that abstinence is not the only solution. I am lucky to have so much family and friend support and I am looking forward to finding a second family here as well.

Do I Have To Give Up My Drinking Friends?

Hello. I'm 32, living in California. I was directed to MM by a 'friend' in a life coaching group, so thought I would give it a try. My significant other (SO) and I love drinking together. It's so much a part of our identity, what we do for fun, and who we choose to be friends with that I am reluctant to cut down although it would be better for me to cut down, and maybe even better for my relationship with my SO. I've realized recently that each time I set a goal for myself to stop after 3 drinks, it never ever happens.

We usually binge drink on average three times per week. Sometimes, we make a decision to abstain for an evening, enjoy a sober activity out such as movies, but we always end up getting our drinking in a day or two later. On binge night, we split a bottle of wine, followed by 3-4 vodka and seltzers for me and 4-5 beers by SO. I know it's too much, but it is pure pleasure for both of us, except for the hangovers the next day. I have a big question about our friendships – do we have to give up all our current friends? I really don't know if I could be completely sober when I'm out with them. Almost everyone I love is a very heavy drinker, so I'm really in a quandary about that. Any feedback would be great.

Problem Drinking For Last Two Years After Lifetime Of Moderate Drinking

Greetings, all. I am very excited to have found MM. For my whole life I have been a moderate drinker but in the last two years have gotten in a habit of way more than moderate drinking. I went through two traumatic events in 2015: my teenaged daughter passed away and my mother (whom I'm close with) was diagnosed with Alzheimer's. It began with having a daily beer after work (no problem there) but then I found that I kept the beer going until the moment I went to bed. I am up to about 6-8 beers per day, every day. It shocks me how quick but gradual the habit caught hold.

Being conscious of drunk driving, I've found myself not wanting to leave the house or run errands after work or on weekends (when I start drinking by mid-afternoon). I just want to get home to that beer. I am definitely becoming less productive around the house and my wife notices. I've grown to like the perpetual buzz while at home. Some people get irritable and aggressive with alcohol, but with me I mellow out and have all the patience in the world.

Good news: I am on day 5 of moderate drinking...2 high

quality beers in the late evening. I enjoy them SO much more. I love the tips-setting your glass down while drinking, and taking sips and not gulps. I still have after-work cravings and have a lot to learn here.

I'm very new, but very excited. I'm sure there will be some back-sliding, but I know moderate drinking is possible with me.

I Want To Cut Back

I've had some challenges with alcohol since I was 20 (I'm 30 now). To the point, I've had a shady history of alcohol abuse. The only times I've been able to really abstain from drinking for an extended period of time have been during my two pregnancies. I don't drink to get drunk every single time I drink, nor do I always drink too much. But it happens more than it should, at least 2-3 times per month. I often regret it later. With horrible all-day hangovers.

When I'm drinking, I also get nasty towards my hubby and we have been fighting due to it. I do not like myself when I drink too much! I'm not my normal loving self. I also don't want to become that mom that can't be there for my babies because I'm drunk! I need some support with keeping my moderating in check! When I think about it, my life is amazing in many ways, so why do I want to throw that away for drunkenness?

I just know if I cut back on my alcohol consumption, I will feel much better about myself and my choices. I don't think it's something I can do without a little support, though, which is what brings me here.

Desperate

I'm new and feeling pretty desperate and alone. My husband absolutely hates that I drink so much and sometimes I feel like he hates me too. My health is suffering and I get miserable hangovers. A friend asked me the other day what it is that I get out of drinking and my answer was I get nothing out of it, not happiness or joy or even feeling all that good anymore. In fact, it makes me feel worse in every way. I need to understand why I still have the urge to drink with no reward from it anymore.

I read the Steps of Change every morning to get it ingrained in my head. I want to think about change rather than when I'm going to have that first or next drink. I want to get through a day without drinking. I want to know what it feels like, I want to be proud of myself, I want to succeed. But I've realized I can't do it alone and I can't do it cold turkey. I desperately want help cutting way down.

FINDING THE POWER TO BEGIN

Many of us come to MM when we feel we are defeated and powerless. We are not alone.

From: *Responsible Drinking: A Moderation Management Approach for Problem Drinker* (https://www.amazon.com/Responsible-Drinking-Moderation-Management-Frederick/dp/B015QL2578)

> Here's what one person, looking into MM, as a way to change a distressing drinking problem, said in an online discussion. He was troubled by a feeling common to those with drinking problems: a loss of power over alcohol. AA takes that feeling to be an unchangeable fact, but this person was seeking a way to regain that power.
>
> 'I am powerless over alcohol. I tell myself that I will not drink, and then I do. I decide that I will not drink during the week, only weekends, but I fall short. Once I start drinking, I

cannot stop. I get annoyed when alcohol runs out or I don't have any when I want it.

My life is unmanageable due to alcohol because my career suffers. I cannot give 100 percent to anything, work or personally related. I say and do embarrassing things that I feel embarrassed about afterward. I suffer from all-day hangovers.

A person who had achieved moderation through MM replied:

'You could call it powerless it feels like powerless. When I really believed it was fun to get drunk, or that I needed to drink to get through my life, then, of course I drank. But the truth is, I set myself up for it. Right now, I am very much involved in changing and re-fixing the strength of my belief.

I think most of us know the power of belief. I think we all have different little particulars about our drinking history or why we do it. We all shared the same beliefs about it. We believed we needed to drink to get through certain situations. We believed, if we drank, we would be happy. By a certain point in our lives we realized more and more that drinking to get through situations could create more and different and bad situations. But somehow, that didn't *necessarily stop us from using it to get away from the bad situations in front of us at the moment. Additionally, we realize that we only feel happy when we're drinking. Maybe it is a function of age, but after a while, I wasn't really happy for too long even while drinking. And I certainly wasn't happy after.*

So, I, like you, set myself up for feeling worse about myself by now saying I was going to do something about my drinking and then drinking anyway and just feeling like a big fat loser. But take heart. This is just part of the process of healing!! It's not easy to change our beliefs and the habits that have evolved over many years. First, we need that inkling. An inkling that all is not as it should be. That inkling needs to be walked around, stared at, thought about, and it grows, slowly, little by little. And works its way into I want to change and transforms itself into I can change and moves on to change. For most of us, I want to change doesn't magically result in change. We have to work the steps, the baby steps everyone talks about.'

This dialogue reflects how hopeless and out of control people can feel when they start to confront a drinking problem. Chances are you've tried sporadically to bring the drinking problem under control, without really giving it your full attention, and failed. But now you're giving the issue a new priority in your life. You're taking the time to focus your attention and efforts in this area. Be aware that, 'to change your beliefs and habits that have evolved over many years,' you've started on a journey that is made up of many small steps. As you take each step forward, your belief and confidence in your own ability to succeed will grow. So far, you have seen that large numbers of people do resolve drinking problems, and that, for many, moderation is a viable alternative to abstinence.

----Frederick Rotgers, Marc F. Kern, Rudy Hoeltzel; Responsible Drinking: A Moderation Management Approach for Problem Drinkers; New Harbinger Publications; 1 edition (September 9, 2002)

We are often asked at MM, "How long will it take? How long before I can approach my drinking with a 'take it or leave it' attitude?" The answer is, we don't know. Each individual is unique and their journey is also unique. Some of us will never obtain a "take it or leave it" attitude toward our drinking but we will obtain the power to make the decision to "take or leave" the drink.

How long does it take to feel more powerful?

As long as it takes to type out your introductory post to one of MM's support communities:

The **MM Forum** (https://forum.moderation.org/).
The **MM Listserv** (http://www.moderation.org/online/mmlist_welcome.html),
The **MM Facebook Group** (https://www.facebook.com/groups/462485394489953)
The **MMabsers Group** (https://groups.yahoo.com/neo/groups/mmabsers/).

Or, attend your first **MM Meeting** (http://moderation.org/meetings/index.html)

Or, start tracking your drinks on **MM's Abstar Drink Counter** (http://moderation.org/abstar/).

Take the step you are capable of taking right now, even if the only step you feel ready for is turning to the next page of this book.

Turn the page.

Take back your power!

CHAPTER 2: NO LONGER TRAVELING ALONE

We just don't get it. We don't understand why such a simple concept as drinking less or not drinking at all has been impossible for us to put into practice. We've tried. Goodness knows we've tried and if the desire to change were enough, we'd have conquered our problem long ago.

What is wrong with us? Why are we so weak? Why are others able to do what we cannot?

If you bring up the subject of moderation with someone who has chosen abstinence and succeeded at abstaining from alcohol for a long period, they will likely reply, "Moderation doesn't work, I should know, I tried to moderate for years. Abstinence is the only answer."

Their statement is correct in saying that most people who finally choose abstinence, do so after struggling to moderate for years on their own. However, one important caveat is missing from their statement, many people struggle to abstain for years on their own also, and many are only able to abstain after they have joined a support group of people who share their same goal. Even then, sustained abstinence does not come immediately for most. The change and transformation that is vital to changing our relationship with alcohol, whether that be through moderation or abstinence, is not a short road trip that we map out on our GPS by choosing the quickest and easiest route, it is a lifelong journey that we commit to, no matter how bumpy the road is or how many detours there are along the way.

It can be overwhelming and defeating on our own, but when we know others are on the road with us, showing us the way, encouraging us through the tough spots, challenging us, and, yes, depending on us, it makes it much more difficult to give up. And, "not giving up" is the most essential tool in our toolbox. We'll talk more about tools and our toolbox in the next chapter.

Peer support is another tool and, while it is true that some people are able to moderate or abstain on their own, for the rest of us, peer support is that tool we didn't know we needed, the one that finally gets the job done when everything else has failed. Most of us reach out for support as our last option…and end up wondering why we waited so long.

Peer support provides many benefits that are just not available to us when we try to "fix" our behavior on our own.

What are the benefits of peer support?

Acceptance: There is nothing like the feeling of recognizing our own pain or shame in someone else's words, whether it be from online posts on the MM forum and Listserv or statements made from fellow MM members at a face-to-face meeting. It is the feeling of finally finding a safe place and knowing we are no longer fighting alone. After years of feeling like we were lost and alone in a crowded world where any admission of a drinking problem is met with either judgment or pressure to take actions we are not able or ready to make, it is a relief to find a place where we can lay down our burden and say, "Here I am, I need your help." and be met with responses such as the following:

"Been there!"

"It gets better."

"We're glad you're here."

"You can do this!"

"You don't have to do anything right now, the fact that you're here, that you reached out, is enough until you figure out what you need to do next."

Accountability: Sharing our goals with others is one of the most powerful tools in the MM toolbox. This is proven by the number of MM members who sign up for the different rosters that have become the backbone of many members' moderate lifestyle. Every day, dozens of people sign up for the daily "Sticky" abs roster, committing to not drink for the day. So many members wouldn't use this tool if they hadn't found it effective in helping them obtain their goals.

No, no one is looking over our shoulders or following us around to make sure we toe the line. At MM we hold ourselves accountable for the promises we make to ourselves and realize that self-honesty is integral to our own self-recovery, or recovery of self. It is much easier to be honest in a non-judgmental, non-expectational environment. Our peers have no expectations of us, our actions do not affect their lives, so being dishonest about any failure to meet the goals we have set for ourselves is ineffective or harmful only to our own recovery.

The pressure is off. So, how does it work then?

It works because when we join MM, we become part of a team and when we join with someone in pursuing a goal or even when we proclaim our individual goal/s to our other team members, we increase our desire to meet those goals, not only for ourselves but for others who might be unsure of their own ability to achieve the same goal. It is a circle. First, we read of others achieving what seems unattainable for ourselves and their success makes it seem attainable for us. Their courage to try for their goals gives us courage to try for our own goals. Then, we set our own goal and share our intentions with our fellow members to give courage to those who are not ready to attempt their own goals—yet.

What happens if we are unsuccessful in achieving our goal?

The circle begins again. We share our "unsuccess" with our peers, which gives them the courage to share their own "un-success stories." Then, when we feel ready to try for our goal again, it gives others the courage to try again.

Self-Compassion: As illustrated in one of the following stories, when we feel compassion for our peers, and we recognize how hard they are trying, it is easier to feel compassion for ourselves.

Community: Some of us may have become isolated because of our drinking. Many of us have experienced changes in our interpersonal relationships. And, most of us will experience some ostracization because of our decision to change our relationship with drinking.

Sometimes it feels like we can't win. We keep drinking, we lose friends and loved ones. We quit drinking, we lose friends and loved ones. MM provides a community that understands what it is like to go through this loss and the tough decisions that need to be made to put our own well-being first.

We're here for each other at times when it feels like the whole world is against us. While we may be very excited to have found a community of people who understand the struggles that we are going through, our families and friends may be skeptical. We've been raised in a society that has been indoctrinated with the belief that abstinence is the only solution for those who are concerned about their drinking, no matter the degree to which a person misuses alcohol. Until recently, the majority of our medical and mental health care providers also supported this belief, even though research has shown that many people can learn to drink moderately.

Why not start where they want to start and go from there?" *ask* the authors of the book, *Beyond Addiction: How Science and Kindness Help People Change* (https://www.amazon.com/Beyond-Addiction-Science-Kindness-People/dp/1476709475). According to them, many people change their drinking patterns outside the confines of the traditional view that complete abstinence is the only effective solution. Contrary to popular opinion, one subgroup that fit alcohol dependent criteria, became unproblematic drinkers without treatment. The authors proceed further to voice their concern that insisting on abstinence for a person who is struggling with substance abuse is unnecessary and can serve as a barrier to seeking help and subsequent positive change.

Although more research has come to the forefront in support of moderation in recent years and more therapists are supportive of their clients' quests for moderation, there are still many people, both lay and professional, who stand by the belief that abstinence is the best choice for not just those who are dependent on alcohol but anyone who drinks too much on a regular basis.

How do we convince them to support us in our own pursuit of moderation? We explain to them that this is the step that we feel capable of taking right now. This step may not take us where we want or need to be, but it *is* a step. We might even mention that approximately 30% of members do eventually choose abstinence, but that the choice was not forced on them, it was one they made based on their own experiences with moderation and—because of MM's recommended abstinence periods as part of a moderate lifestyle—their loss of fear of living an alcohol-free life.

We can also invite them to read the stories in this book and on the MM Forum to acquaint themselves with the members of the MM community and discover for themselves that MM members are not people who are continuing to willfully drink problematically under the guise of pursuing moderation. We are people who approach every day with the goal of drinking within functional, healthy limits. We work at it, we use tools and we seek support and guidance.

Do we always realize our goals?

No.

However, with the support of the MM community and the support of those closest to us in our day-to-day life, most of us realize significant reduction in our drinking and an improvement in our life.

STORIES

Maisie's Story

I found MM in September, 2014. I thought what I was going through was uniquely shameful and awful, but I have now heard this story many, many times. I was a binge drinker in college, and adulthood didn't solve the problem. For a long time, I was a weekend social drinker, but when I drank, I drank a lot.

As we got older, we started buying better wine. Slowly, my husband and I got into the habit of opening a bottle of wine almost every night and splitting it. Not infrequently, we opened another during the evening. If there were guests, many bottles were opened. I slept badly and woke up every morning vowing not to drink again that day. By evening that resolution was gone. I kept telling myself that if I didn't get my drinking under control, I'd have to stop entirely, which seemed impossible and scary.

I don't remember how I found MM, but I think I was just surfing the web looking for help. I was surprised that such a thing existed and so happy to find others who were struggling with the same issues I had. I first hung out on the forums, bought Responsible Drinking and started reading. Later, I found the Listserv and I haven't looked back. The idea that I might be able to solve my drinking problems without ending up at AA made me so happy.

After a rather drunken wedding weekend, I started a 30. I made it through the whole 30, but I've only done one more, a Dryuary last year. I completed that first 30 and I don't remember it being terribly hard. I think I was flying along on the idea that after this 30, I'd be able to drink and it wouldn't make me miserable.

Amazingly, that really has happened.

The next step after the 30 was trying to figure out what moderation was going to look like for me and how I was going to get there. I worked my way up to trikes, (3 days abstaining in a week) then f'abs, (4 in a week) then started working on the number of drinks on my drinking days. I started making rules for myself. The first one was no drinking alone. Then, no drinking after I came home from any place where I had been drinking. (I broke that one twice recently and regretted it both times.)

My current program is mostly BTB though I sign up for trikes and f'abs every week. BTB is helpful right now because I'm having more trouble with the number of drinks per occasion than the number of days per week. I'm pretty comfortable with three or four non-drinking days a week. Lately, I've been happy to notice that I'll have five or six non-drinking days if I don't have social events with alcohol coming up. While BTB for women allows three drinks per day, I really need to stick to two - always. When I let myself get to three, I don't sleep well and don't feel my best in the morning.

This is my current struggle. It's so hard to turn down drink number three when the wine is good and the company is fun. I find I do it more and more, though, because I'm better at remembering how good it feels not to overdo.

This is still very much a process for me. I haven't yet really decided whether I am okay with drinking every day on vacation. I did that on a winter vacation and regretted it because the everyday drinking led me to drinking too much on the last few days of the vacation. So, I'll be experimenting with a few abs days on vacation this year.

I don't know where all this will lead. It surprised me that I've been here almost five years, I thought it was three! Maybe in five more it will feel natural and I'll be a moderate drinker without so much monitoring. Even if I have to keep monitoring, it's more than worth it. My reaction to overdrinking is almost always hangxiety which is SO unpleasant and now it's very rare and may disappear altogether eventually. I can live with my current level of drinking if that's what I can do.

Two relevant points: One is that Abstar did not work for me. The constant planning and recording just felt too hard. However, signing up for the trikes, f'abs and BTB rosters have been lifesaving. MM has developed so many tricks and pathways that some of it will work for all of us. Second, I could not have done this without this community. I wish I were as good at supporting others as some of you are (looking at you, HL), but between my schedule and my introversion, I am often lurking. But, without the members of MM, I would not be where I am. Everyone's courage to continue to fight has contributed to my own courage to fight, whether I acknowledged it or not. My gratitude is huge, and I consider you all deeply connected to me. Thank you.

RB's Story: Fox Day

> *Yesterday what got me spiraling down was my husband pointing out a spot on our back yard, looking out from our big living room windows, saying that's where the fox was sitting the other day. I said what fox? He looked at me kind of funny and said, you know, the one when I said come out here there's a fox out back. I said, yeah, but that was a few years ago, right? He said no, just within the last few weeks. When we looked at his phone and the pictures the date was May 10, Mothers Day. The last day I drank before I started this abs period, two days before I reconnected with the MM site and three before I signed up.*

> I was horrified. I went and got out my journal and realized what day that was and that I had been too drunk to remember about the fox. I was a tad relieved when he clarified that he figured I had missed seeing it, because by the time I got to the window it had run around the side of the house, and I did then fuzzily remember going to another window to try to catch it, but up to that point I had no memory of any fox discussion. From his pictures it was a gorgeous animal, orange with some brown (a cross fox) and a lush bushy tail tipped with white. So sorry I missed it. Maybe next time I won't
>   --RB's MM Forum Post, June 2015

Greetings and salutations to everyone doing this important work to make their lives, and thereby the lives of everyone around them, and indeed the whole world, better.

It's been a long time since I've visited the MM Forum, but I'm still working on my moderation project and still logging into Abstar.

Today is my third anniversary of Fox Day, the day that launched me on this long and amazing trip toward being who I am.

Three years ago today, May 10, 2015, was my last major blackout (with maybe two exceptions) from drinking. That day a beautiful cross fox walked through our backyard. My husband told me about it a few days later; I had been too drunk to remember seeing it, so he showed me pictures he'd taken. I did know I had been extremely drunk. I was so embarrassed, I hated myself and how I was losing day after day—days I could never get back. I was losing my life! My blackouts were happening more than weekly; I was not a binge drinker or a daily drinker, I was a daily binge drinker. I am not sure how I got that way, but it took a very long time, starting maybe in high school, and I think I was having worse and worse effects every time I drank. I knew, even before I knew I'd missed seeing that fox, that I had to make a change. I was scared shirtless. The next day I joined MM and started my first (and so far only) 31-day abstinence period.

I wanted to write this story in hopes of encouraging others who might be struggling and feeling discouraged by what they might feel is slow progress in getting a handle on their drinking problem.

The rest of that year was exciting, scary, exhilarating, discouraging; sometimes I felt smug, sometimes abject. It was difficult to see the MM limits as reasonable for me, but I kept working on it. I had so many wonderful people here helping me and encouraging me, every step of the way. I'll never forget Bee Brown, Kary May, Kenny, Nils, ThreeD, Bruce, Astrid, Bonnie, Leon, Donna and Yolanda for their understanding, connection, commiseration, encouragement and gentle corrections as time went on. To you and others I may not have named, thank you so much.

During my second year I started to develop some solid strategies and routines that really helped solidify my progress and my resolve to never return to my old drinking habits. I stopped drinking while making dinner. I indulged myself with other treats to distract me, such as delicious non-alcoholic beverages so I could still enjoy the ritual of having that late afternoon drink, and I was a heavy supporter of the ice cream industry. I still hit red numbers but I was able to effectively use the calendar with its new months and new weeks to try, try again and to devise new approaches—sometimes some fun challenges for myself—and to reach out to form some one-on-one and small-group support networks. I always count my drinks. My total drink count for the full calendar year of 2016 was 795.

During my third year, I got better about sticking to a weekly habit of Sunday–Monday abs days to start the week. I still like that but don't do it totally consistently. I found that going outside to get fresh air and paying attention to my breathing helped me get through some of the cravings. I found I was genuinely looking forward to seeing friends and to various activities that had nothing to do with drinking. This was new! I found that, even though I never pulled off another real 30 (I did a 26 that was supposed to be a 30 in November 2015), I enjoy abstaining for shorter periods, like 7s and 9s, to keep my tolerance low and my appreciation of the good things in my life high. I am finding it easier all the time, but it's not a days or weeks or months type of process, it's a years and decades type of project. My total drink count for 2017 was 488.

Now I'm starting my fourth year as a moderate drinker. I think I'm really getting it now, and even though I have my lapses, they're nothing like the old lapses. My goal, which I am planning to continue working on for the indefinite future, is to stay within BTB limits, to go for a one per day average and to not go into the red numbers anymore. I have recently kept my red numbers down to 4s and sometimes 5s but now I want to cut those reds out entirely because I can tell when I wake up the next day that I went red and it's never worth whatever fun it might have been the night before. I hate feeling hungover. Hangover avoidance is my strongest motivation. Other motivations are that I don't have to worry that I said or did something stupid that I need to apologize for to whoever might have been present. I know my health is better and that my quality of life is better now and in the future thanks to not drinking heavily. I enjoy a cocktail before and/or a glass of wine at dinner, and more and more that is a great plenty. It's nice to be able to enjoy alcohol in moderation, knowing it's not killing me. My relationships are better, I enjoy life so much more, all the time, than the fun times I used to think I was having drinking.

I have MM and its people to thank for the life I have now, because if total cold turkey abstinence was my only option, which I used to think it was, I may never have even started to deal with my drinking problem. If you are working on this, whether you end up managing moderation or you decide abstinence is your best option, just know that time is on your side and getting it is one of the best things you can do for yourself. Keep working at it and you will get it.

Cheers!

Horse Lover's Story: Compassion and Resilience

Before I found Moderation Management all I knew about getting help for my problem drinking was abstinence only programs, and that scared the bjeezus out of me. If I tried one of those and failed (i.e. had one drink), then there was no hope for me. "I might lose everything including my family, my health and even my life, but I'm too scared to try something in case I fail." Pretty flawed logic, I know. That middle of the night, heart pounding, head aching, nausea rising, hands shaking, anxiety spiraling out of control thinking is not always rational.

In the middle of one of those nights though, I somehow stumbled upon Moderation Management, and my life has been forever changed. That night I bumbled my way through the website and finally found the listserv. There I read posts from people who were facing exactly the same awful, hideous, shameful problem I faced, and they were cracking jokes, making up songs, holding virtual hands, freewheeling through days of abstaining and weeks of moderation like it was some gigantic carnival game. They were also weeping on each other's shoulder, offering words of encouragement, and whispering little pearls of grace. When someone drank when they didn't plan to, or drank too much, they were wrapped in virtual warm hugs, held tight for support, and reminded that today is brand new. These kind people were practicing what I now recognize as compassion. Pema Chodron teaches us that, "Compassion is not a relationship between the healer and the wounded. It's a relationship between equals. Only when we know our own darkness well can we be present with the darkness of others. Compassion becomes real when we recognize our shared humanity."

Compassion. That's the first thing I learned at MM. And you want to know how I learned about compassion? It's actually a three-step process that constantly repeats. Step one was when I wrote my first post introducing myself and sharing my dark secret, I was greeted with open arms and warm hearts. There was common understanding, shared experience, and grace. I didn't need to be perfect. I didn't need to conquer my problem in one day or one week or even in one year. I didn't have to do it the way someone else prescribed. I got to take steps in my time and in any direction I chose, and no one judged me. If I strayed off my intended path, I was welcomed back with those same open hearts. I was redeemed through compassion. The next thing you know (okay, actually a few weeks later) I was the one welcoming a newbie, telling her that she was in the right place, that she was going to be doing some hard work, and that she would be fine. She wasn't a screw up; she made a misstep. She was a good and valuable human being with all the messiness that entails. That was step two. The third step took a few months. You know those horrible, monstrous things you say to yourself in the middle of the night after too much alcohol? That's called Negative Self Talk (NST). That was pretty much an every night occurrence for me. But after I'd been at MM for a few months, I realized that I wasn't engaging in that disgusting NST anymore! What?!? Seems I had learned to offer compassion for myself by feeling it first for others. I mean, I had the same ghastly problem they had, and they were amazing, wise, kind, funny, smart human beings, so...I must be too! Wow! How cool is that?

The second thing I learned at MM was about resilience. There is a quote that is often attributed to Winston Churchill (who said something similar) but was first actually written, ironically, in a 1938 Anheuser-Busch ad, "...They found contentment in the thrill of action, knowing that success was never final and failure never fatal. It was courage that counted." Boy howdy, does that pertain to my journey at MM.

I remember the first time I literally white-knuckled my way through a single night of abstaining. It was brutal, and at the time all I could think of was how messed up I was that I couldn't get through one night without alcohol. But the next day...ta da! Look at me! I did it! I set a goal and I succeeded! What a feeling! Then I did it again! Woot! Then I...didn't do it again. I was going to abstain that night, but instead I drank. And I drank too much. I had failed. But when I shared my "failure" on the listserv the reaction was, of course, compassion. Yeah, I didn't do what I had planned to do. But today I could make a new plan, bolstered by some tips and tricks from some old timers, plus what I had learned from the previous day, and voila! I had another opportunity to succeed. I could focus on that "failure" and let it pull me down, or I could focus on my previous success and move forward. Resilience.

Through my years here at MM I have cut my drinking from about 35 per week to about 9-12 per week. The 12 is a little higher than I want it to be, and I'm working on that. Abstaining days are, in general, a lot easier than when I first started. Moderate drinking days are usually that: moderate. Sometimes I fall short of my goal, whether it is for one day or one week, and sometimes I exceed my goal. Some days are harder, some days are easier. But on the whole, when I look at where I started and where I am today, it's nothing short of a miracle. Am I successful? In my book, that's a big loud Yes!

Summer1's Story: Back to Normal

Years ago, I was a moderate drinker without putting much effort into it. Although I'd had a few (or maybe more than a few) experiences with excessive drinking in my youth, I toned it down as an adult. There may have been a few instances of going a little overboard at a party, but for the most part, my drinking felt normal enough.

I remember once arriving at a party when I was in my early twenties, a bit late because of work, but it was still fairly early, maybe an hour into Friday cocktails. It was obvious as soon as I walked in that some people were already well into party mode in a way that did not bode well, and I can remember quite clearly looking around at people I'd known forever, my generation as well as my parents' generation, the ones who were always fun and sociable at a party and the ones who would get loud or argumentative, and realizing that I was going to have to be careful which group I ended up in. I asked for a soda, and one of my hosts asked, "Don't you want a gin and tonic?" I said I'd start out with just soda, and then have something else later. And that's what I did. It's still a vivid memory for me because I have seen, through the years, how drinking turned out for some of those people. Some of them are people I still enjoy drinking with these days, and some are in serious trouble with alcohol.

Another instance that sticks out in my mind from that time was visiting a friend who always said whatever was on her mind, to the point sometimes of being a bit nosy. Also, she was studying to be a doctor, so I guess she felt entitled to ask questions about health. She asked how much I was drinking.

"Oh, five to seven drinks," I replied.

"Oh, no, that's way too much! That's really dangerous!"

"What? That's a beer most days, maybe two drinks one weekend day, and some days with nothing at all! How can that be too much?"

"In a week? OMG I thought you meant every day!"

Well, somewhere between those days and my fifties, something changed. It snuck up gradually, but it was getting to a point I didn't like at all, when it seemed like I was going to end up in the group of people who just shouldn't drink. I kept telling myself that I would have to quit entirely, but I really didn't want to do that, so I didn't do anything. A couple of years went by like that before I stumbled across MM.

It was a huge relief to find that MM offered something between the pattern I was stuck in and giving up alcohol entirely. I felt, for the first time in years, that there was a path to get back to the kind of moderate drinking that I had enjoyed previously. However, it was a struggle to get started. The first few months just seemed so painful.

The first thing that helped me was counting drinks. Honestly, I was embarrassed to admit even to myself how much I was drinking, so I cut back a bit before I started counting, just so I wouldn't have to record such high numbers. I started really observing my drinking like it was a science project, noticing my patterns, habits, and feelings in a way I had been avoiding for quite a while. I was also paying close attention to the drinking patterns of those around me, the good examples as well as the cautionary tales. I learned a huge amount from participating in the MM forums and gradually was able to build up some better habits and strategies so that I could chip away at my excessive drinking.

It turns out that for me, chipping away at it was the way to go. For various reasons, it seemed impossible to commit to 30 days of abstinence, but MM forum members encouraged me to do whatever worked for me. "Baby steps." That was the mantra that worked best for me at the beginning.

Baby steps: delaying the first drink, pacing, alternating alcoholic drinks with water, practicing mindfulness, reading about what worked for different people, trying out some of their strategies, adjusting as I went along-- all those things were important. But really, the main key was the support and encouragement of so many people on the forum.

After six months of baby steps, my consumption was considerably reduced, if still well above the MM guidelines, and I was ready for my first Oneuary, a January of onesies. It was certainly a challenge to limit myself to one drink at a time, but it was a challenge I felt ready to embrace, rather than forcing myself into it.

Despite having a tropical family vacation mid-month, I managed to come close enough to feel that I had accomplished something significant. That January marked the beginning of what's now 18 months of keeping my average daily consumption at 1 drink or less...not always exactly even, as some weeks might have had 10 drinks and then the next week less, but it's better all the time.

In other words, I am back where I started, at 7 drinks a week, as in my younger days. It's not quite as easy these days, but really, what is? Some of what I've learned in MM, I already knew, just like I knew way back then to start with a soda to avoid overdoing it at a party, and some of it has been new. It's still a struggle sometimes to stick with healthy limits, but overall, it's great. I needed some reminders, some new strategies, and a lot of support to get myself back to a healthier way of drinking. I am so thankful to the many MM forum members who have helped me along the way.

CHAPTER 3: TOOLS

The initial perception most people have regarding moderate drinking is that it requires a lifetime of counting, measuring, tracking and planning. This is not an inaccurate perception—moderate drinking does require awareness of how much we drink, how often and under what circumstances. However, there are several techniques, or tools as we call them, that effectively decrease the amount we drink that do not require counting.

But first, let's talk about counting, measuring, tracking and planning.

Counting and Measuring: It is crucial, in the beginning of our moderation journey, to gain an accurate, honest knowledge of how much we drink. Keeping track and recording the number of **standardized drinks** (https://www.rethinkingdrinking.niaaa.nih.gov/How-much-is-too-much/What-counts-as-a-drink/Whats-A-

Standard-Drink.aspx) we drink per day and per week gives us a baseline from which we can plan the initial steps we will take toward our moderate drinking goal. Many of us are surprised to discover that our favorite cocktail or IPA beer actually adds up to two or three standard drinks and the amount we drink nightly or weekly is two to three times MM's recommended moderate drinking limits.

From MM's Steps of Change (Appendix A):

> For Men: No more than 14 drinks per week, and no more than 4 per occasion.
> For Women: No more than 9 drinks per week, and no more than 3 per occasion.
> For Both: Do not drink on more than 3-4 days per week. Research has shown that these limits are generally workable for persons who have learned to moderate after experiencing drinking problems. These limits are mostly the same as those set forth by the US government's National Institute for Alcohol Abuse and Alcoholism. However, NIAAA gives a similar but slightly lower weekly limit for women of 7 drinks per week (with the same 3 per occasion), so women might want to adopt that lower weekly limit.
> Note that these are upper limits rather than usual quantities. A usual quantity for a moderator is more likely to

> be 1-2 drinks per occasion, as a matter of individual choice.
> Blood alcohol levels are critical, since judgment and control
> are progressively lost at higher levels. Also, alcohol causes
> most of its physical damage at higher blood levels. MM sets
> 0.055% as the upper limit for blood alcohol concentration.
> As well as the quantity consumed, the pace of drinking
> directly affects blood alcohol

Tracking: Keeping a record of when we drink, the circumstances under which we drink, and how much we drink per occasion provides the necessary knowledge to distinguish when our drinking is habit driven such as grabbing a beer from the fridge the minute we walk in the door from work or pouring a glass of wine every time we start cooking dinner, *or* trigger driven such as sneaking a couple of drinks before a social event (pre-gaming) to reduce social anxiety or repeatedly drinking too much around certain family members or friends.

Identifying when and why we drink too much is integral to learning which tools to use to combat our over-drinking in specific situations. A habit can be replaced by another healthier action. A trigger can be avoided or addressed without the use of alcohol.

Another important task of Tracking is providing an accurate record of our process. Too many times when we fail to reach our goal in the time frame we desire, we think we have failed. In fact, we have *failed* to recognize the improvement and progress we *have* made in pursual of our goals. Tracking provides indisputable proof of our progress.

Less is less and better is better.

Planning: "Fail to plan, plan to fail" is a popular slogan we often hear in MM. Planning is especially important at the beginning of our journey when we are learning a new way of life and the old way is still so alluring, before new habits and routines have become well-established. Planning doesn't only include setting a specific drink limit for a certain day, it also includes preparing mentally and physically for the task we have set for ourselves. Have we decided what we're going to do instead of heading to the fridge for a beer right after work? Have we stocked up on alternative NA beverages? Do we have a plan for all that time we used to spend drinking? Have we taken time to fully appreciate and imagine the benefits that changing our drinking habit could bring to our lives?

Many MM members use the <u>MM Abstar Drink Counter</u> (http://moderation.org/abstar/) which can be used for counting, tracking *and* planning since it allows you to pre-enter your drinking amounts in advance. It also incorporates the Accountability Tool with its public roster, however, members can request a private Abstar row if they choose.

There are several free mobile drink counter apps available also.

ENOUGH WITH THE COUNTING!

Thinking of all that counting and tracking and planning <u>can</u> be daunting. The good news is there are tools and routines we can introduce into our lives that will not only effectively decrease our drinking but also make it more difficult to over-drink. These tools are diverse and adaptable. For the Moderation Month 2019 Campaign on Facebook, a new "non-counting tool" was introduced every day for 30 days! (See Appendix B: Toolbox)

Some of them are simple:

The Delay Tool: Delay the time you start drinking by one hour, or, if you are going to a social event, mingle for an hour, perhaps with an NA

NA-N-Between Tool: Drink 1 NA beverage—your choice—between alcoholic drinks. Remember, be prepared by having your favorite NA drink available. Water works and it keeps us hydrated.

Stop 1 hour early: Establish a bedtime routine that does not include alcohol. You will come to treasure this.

Others require a little more thought.

If and But Tool: Finish the following sentences, "If I drink this drink, I will_____?" "But if I don't drink this drink, I will _____?"

Buddy-Up Tool: Find someone who has the same goal as you and Buddy-Up to help both of you achieve success.

Toothbrush Tool: That's right, your simple toothbrush, doesn't just fight cavities, it fights cravings by getting that lingering taste out of your mouth so your brain doesn't keep expecting more. Brushing your teeth at night, sends a signal to the brain that you are done imbibing, whether that be of sugar or wine or whatever your poison. It's surprisingly effective, have you ever drank a glass of wine right after brushing your teeth? Blech!

We don't have to pack our toolbox full at the very beginning. We can pick out one or two that we feel comfortable using and we feel will be most effective right now.

STORIES

Peggy's Story:

I joined MM on 9/15/17. Before that, I had been a heavy drinker with many black-out nights. I started seeing a therapist to help me, but I just succeeded in pretending that I was moderating, with no change in my drinking patterns.

Enter MM. Something clicked in my brain/body. I realized that I had a serious problem and that I had to change. Somehow, from the first day I joined, I started to moderate. This is not to say it was easy...I had many nights of temptation, whether it was an abs night or a moderate night. My husband was a great help, but on many nights when I was abstaining he didn't, and that was often hard. But I absed anyway.

I wrote my own spreadsheet to keep track of my drinks. I am very competitive, especially with myself, so having the spreadsheet and seeing my drinking numbers helped immensely, as did joining the streaker roster.

Except for vacations, I have been BTB (By the Book, or according to MM guidelines) since 9/15/17. On vacation, I consciously decided that I would not be BTB, but instead that I would drink every day, but never more than 3 drinks on any day. When I returned from vacation, I went back to BTB, even though that was sometimes difficult.

I must say that the support from the great people at MM has helped me be successful, and that I don't think I could have done this without the help and support of my husband.

Boy, do I remember those times of waking up and wondering whether I had a fight with DH (Darling Husband) and what happened and what did I say, etc!!! Horrible times. They (and DH) pushed me to a wonderful therapist who supports MM and pushed me to it. I had a WTF just about a year ago and went, with DH, to my therapist (who I had been seeing for probably a year already but resisting change!) and resisted and fought (with both of them) and then came home and joined MM. This was September 15, 2017, a Friday. Somehow, all that had gone before clicked in me. I realized that I HAD to change (the sneaking, the drinking, the lying) and I was determined to be BTB. I knew I didn't want to abs (I had already done a 30, with DH, the previous April). And somehow it worked for me. I became successfully BTB until my birthday trip to Paris, in February 2018, when I decided to not be BTB for that week. However, I rarely went over 4 drinks on any day and that rarely was on my birthday. When we came back, I was back to BTB. It sounds like it was easy, but it wasn't and still isn't. I still think about drinking, but I don't drink too much. And I'm much happier (and so is DH!)

Dusty Water's Story: The Lesson I Wish I had Learned in School

Some people find school a chore, but I have always been an avid student. Gifted programs in elementary school through honors in graduate school, it seemed my education was fairly complete. However, as a fortysomething-year-old looking back, it's clear that one very important lesson, one that could have saved so much heartache, was completely missing.

I embarked upon a career in sales in a very male dominated industry in my early 20's. I was confident, ok - cocky, and an immediate success. I traveled the country giving presentations to large audiences at conferences and as my reputation as a quality speaker and industry expert grew; so did my reputation as a party girl.

There was no shortage of places, events, and parties to drink. Everyone drank heavily and I was right there alongside them. Keeping up with the boys gave me a feeling of belonging and equality - but of course that was a myth. When I got drunk, people noticed, remembered, and gossiped. When men got drunk, they were team-building and it was globally accepted. I was so sure of my place in the crowd, I didn't notice this double-edged sword that would cut me many times in the coming years.

I cringe to remember too many days standing at the trade show booth so hungover I could barely function. So many nights getting back to my hotel room wondering how I even made it back.

So many stories of other girls getting into trouble and losing their jobs – I was always grateful not to be one of them but I couldn't seem to stop my drunken revelry.

Over the years, I had to make several apologies to those I offended, several emails to my bosses promising it would never happen again. But it did keep happening. I didn't know how to stop so I evaded. I just went to my hotel room, hid, but that didn't fly because part of my job was to socialize, so I continued to white knuckle every night out, hoping that I wouldn't draw attention to myself or humiliate myself, yet again....

Finally, it came to a head.

I had a boss who called me out on my behavior immediately. Then it happened again and I got my first visit from human resources to discuss my drinking. It was the most humiliating and scary time in my life. To lose my job – my career, my home, my wonderful life, and my pride....it was devastating, but it was also the wake -up call I needed.

I knew I didn't want to quit drinking so I looked into alternatives and found Moderation Management and found a community going through the same thing I was – that was so comforting – I was not alone! I read the book <u>Responsible Drinking</u> and the light bulb went on. Counting my drinks, making myself be in the moment with alcohol and slowing down when I felt good. I learned to disappear at parties – sneak away when I realized I was getting drunk. Over time, my colleagues started to call me the Ghost, and it was the best nickname I ever earned. I got very good at these tactics and brought them into my personal life. I was no longer the drunkest person at a party. I actually enjoyed talking to my friends and laughing at other drunkards, so happy and grateful it was not me....at least that time.

I was still nervous about business trips, but I kept practicing. I kept my mind aware, I chanted mantras to myself, I reminded myself not to get drunk, not to have more than one drink in an hour, never to order a martini...Bit by bit, I have been able to go into these situations with confidence that I will not fail, I will not wake up ashamed, I will not feel the need to apologize to anyone about my behavior again.

And, it's been working. I have several years of appropriate behavior under my belt. I still count, I still chant, and I still check in with myself constantly. The vigil will never end and I am perfectly fine with the rituals. I need them, I lean on them, and they give me strength.

This is the lesson I wish I had learned in school. An honest and realistic approach to dealing with alcohol in our society. I know now I am not alone in this struggle. I know others share my shame and self-loathing and many don't know how to break the cycle.

When I was young, I thought adults had it all figured out. I didn't understand that my real learning would start in my thirties. In my forties I am finally feeling like an adult. Sometimes this late maturation makes me feel pathetic. But the more I share with others, a different story emerges; one of lifelong education, successes, failures, and near misses. Now I am looking forward to my fifties - who knows what future lessons are in store for me?

And I wouldn't have it any other way.

Kelsey's Story: Sharing the Moderate Path

Before January 1st, 2014, I used to play a rather grim game with myself: if I could take back one night when I drunkenly embarrassed myself or blacked out (or both), which night would it be? Would it be when I choked on a piece of steak at a work dinner and had to be given the Heimlich maneuver in full view of a roomful of apoplectic guests? Would it be when I solicited a random man to take home (I vaguely remember him awkwardly backing out of the house when he realized how sloshed I was), or when I lost my memory—and my passport—at a bar after a graduate school reading?

On that New Year's, though, the winning answer became clear when I woke up in the emergency room, after having left a holiday party in the wee hours. Petrified and physically sick, I shuffled over to the orderly and asked him to call my boyfriend, who showed up in a taxi thirty minutes later. My boyfriend was angry and disheartened, but he wore his disappointment lightly, seeing how much agony I was in. For days afterward, as I lay in bed and sobbed, berating myself, aloud to him and in my head, every waking moment. After a week of this, I decided things had to change for the sake of my sanity and my relationship, so I cut myself a deal: I would try Moderation Management, a program I had recently read about in a *New York Times* op-ed, for six months. If I blacked out or lost control at all during that time period, I would have to give up drinking immediately, and for good.

There were a few reasons why I didn't initially choose an abstinence-based program. Some of them were philosophical gripes with AA, over their lack of diagnostic clarity and their one-size-fits-all dogma; some were my suspicions that my sudden blackouts were at least partially the result of medications I took, or were age-appropriate, given that many of my peers were doing equally stupid things while drunk. But the major reason I didn't want to be abstinent was that I had spent much of my teen years struggling with anorexia, so the thought of labeling one substance "bad" and entirely off-limits felt a little too reminiscent of the black-and-white thinking endemic to my eating disorder. I wanted to be a person who could be moderate in *all* facets of my life, with respect to *all* substances. Sometimes I worried I was leaning on my past too readily in an attempt to keep alcohol in my life, but I figured I would find that out soon enough, if I wasn't able to stick to my plan. On a dreary winter Wednesday afternoon, I dragged myself to a nondescript rehearsal room in a midtown Manhattan high-rise, and sobbed as I told the women present of my most recent, dangerous escapade. They looked on sympathetically; one handed me a box of tissues.

Every week thereafter, I religiously returned to the meeting. With the encouragement of the other attendees, I formulated a strict plan for myself: I started with a thirty-day period of abstinence, followed by months of drinking within strict boundaries. I learned all the tricks of the trade: show up to events late, start with water, pace yourself with the slowest drinker, order beverages that appeared alcoholic so you couldn't convince yourself that you were the resident buzzkill and you had to order a beer for the other guests' sake. Stay hyper-aware while imbibing: what is pleasurable about this experience? What is not pleasurable? Could the same enjoyment be experienced while sipping a juice? Do you feel that tipping point, after which you no longer have any desire to moderate? Remind yourself over and over why you never again want to wake up awash in shame. Lean on people for support, but go confidently forward, knowing you have the tools within yourself, both to define a healthy drinking plan and to execute it.

There was no true white light conversion moment for me throughout this process: instead, slowly, almost imperceptibly, I felt my body become more aware of, and repulsed by, the negative effects of alcohol. When I drank to satisfaction, I felt a light, pleasant buzz, the corporeal equivalent of cicadas chirping on a warm summer evening. I never once went over my self-imposed limits, but I was able to vividly recall the feeling of sickening intoxication--the impending headache, the stomach-churning nausea--and contrast it with this new, lovely one. Eventually, I didn't have to remind myself of why this new way was better than my old one: drinking moderately, which I once found nearly impossible to do, became second nature, even without the draconian (though beneficial) limits I once imposed. Now, I drink more or less according to feeling, and have not had an incident in more than five years.

I continued to attend the same Moderation Management meeting weekly until soon after I got married to the man who picked me up from the emergency room that dark New Year's Day. After our wedding, we moved to London, where I ran the city's first MM group for almost two years (Brits have very dysfunctional attitudes toward booze!) only stopping after the birth of my first child. Numerous times over those two years, a young woman wandered in and tearfully poured out her terrible, sad tale to the group: she had too much to drink, she hurt herself, she put herself in harm's way, she was scared and sad and she didn't know what to do. And I would listen, hand her tissues and say, "Let me tell you my story."

MM Member's Story: No More Liquor Store Rotation!

When I first got serious about reducing my alcohol consumption, I was drinking dail, and had reached a point where opening a bottle of wine meant drinking a bottle of wine—and I was opening a lot of wine. For some time, I had been rotating wine purchases among several grocery and liquor stores so store clerks wouldn't know how much I was drinking. At least I hoped they wouldn't know... One of my stores had semiannual "case discount" sales, so twice a year I picked up a case of wine, happy that 1) buying a case was expected during such an event so no need to feel self-conscious and 2) for at least a while (usually a very short while) I could take a break from plotting and scheming to avoid detection as a "wino."

Eventually, I began experiencing a few minor health issues that I suspected were related to drinking, and worried that more serious and potentially irreversible problems were inevitable if something didn't change. So, I began trying to cut back. I set limits for myself. I removed all alcohol from the house and forced myself to go out and purchase wine every time I wanted to drink. I was thrilled to find that wine came in 500 ml packages because, even if I drank the whole thing, it was only 2/3 of a bottle! That's progress, right? I was moderately successful, for a while. However, I still said horrible things to myself when I slipped and felt as though I was the only person in the universe experiencing such struggles.

Ultimately, a friend suggested that I go online to look for support, which is how I found Moderation Management (MM). As a serious introvert and no fan of social media (not on Face Book, Twitter, or Instagram), the idea of becoming involved with this online community was daunting, so I lurked. And while lurking, I found that what I thought were uniquely my struggles, weren't unique to me at all. There were many on the site who faced the same challenges, had the same thoughts, and behaved the same way in relation to alcohol. So, I became a regular on the site. I don't post much, but I read everything. There is so much wisdom freely shared, and the tools and rosters have been invaluable.

My initial streak of By the Book (BTB) moderate drinking lasted about six months. Then came the holiday season followed by a long, cold, dark winter and I started slipping. It is now spring, but it has been a cool, gray and rainy spring, and I'm still clawing my way back to extended BTB drinking levels. No, I'm not yet where I want to be in relation to alcohol. I'm not even as satisfied with my progress today as I was six months ago. The path to "success" is not always linear.

Although the progress report remains mixed for now, there are so many ways my life has improved, and I am confident that I possess the knowledge, tools, experience, and support to continue towards my personal goal. Even when I feel like I'm backsliding, I still drink less, and less often than I did before – and I don't say such horrible things to myself when I do slip. Today there are six bottles of wine in the wine rack, most of which have been there for over a month. The liquor store rotation is no longer necessary, so I gave it up months ago. I stay close to MM, where I can share the satisfactions and the challenges of this journey with others who understand and empathize. I'm no longer fighting this battle alone. There is finally light at the end of the tunnel, which is something I did not see when I arrived at this place.

Bob's Story: An Arsenal of Tools

I walked into an AA meeting in lower Manhattan some10 to 12 years ago and immediately felt as if I was "guilty" of something. Standing up and stating your name and "situation" sounded like an indictment. I never went back. It just didn't work for me.

I walked into an MM meeting 2 years ago in Midtown and immediately felt "welcomed" and a part of something that I could relate to weekly. It worked!

I had struggled for years to control my drinking. Ups and downs with no set plan to moderate. I find drinking to be something to do to celebrate the good times or when things aren't going quite as well as I'd like. However, I was always proud of myself to never reach for a drink when something was drastically wrong, like the basement flooding, or being laid off, the death of a close family member (even the election of someone I'm not particularly fond of). Things like that.

What Moderation Management taught me was that it's OK to be me. And for everyone attending the meeting or seeking advice, that it's OK to be yourself. We're human. We make mistakes. We get back up and dust ourselves off. We don't need to pile on personal guilt.

My year-long experience was that we learn from each other; we help each other; we support each other. And it was very much appreciated. My wife said I came home in a better mood after attending an MM meeting.

In time, the long commute post-work made it difficult to remain part of the group. I've had tremendous support from my wife for about a year now and doing "fair." I do keep my limits – hard and soft – in mind. And, in better news, the monthly expenses at the local liquor store are way down.

Counting drinks. Measuring pours. Delaying drinking. Water in between drinks. Eating before drinking. All seem simple and I found they can be once I got in the habit of following these great tips from MM. It took me a while, but I noticed a difference.

Oh, and less drinking keeps the calorie count down as well – one more benefit!

I miss my Tuesday meetings – it was a day that I didn't have a drink. And that was a good thing. But I'm glad that I recognize the need to limit my drinking and to always keep that in mind, whether at social events or home alone. Thank you, MM!

I send my very best wishes to my fellow members.

Rising Force's Story: From Powerless to Empowered

"If we can measure mother nature, we can conquer her."
—Descartes

Correlate: If we can measure our behavior, we can manage it. "You can't manage what you don't measure." Corporate axiom.

In my early forties I began to recognize that I was creating problems by drinking excessively, too frequently, and on inappropriate occasions. I was a corporate hotshot for a Fortune 5 company, and I was producing. Alcohol flowed frequently in work events. I did though adhere to some simple rules about drinking around leadership. 1) Drink 1 fewer than the boss or his executive assistant, and 2) If the leadership is drinking heavily, stay distinctly in control while feigning excessive drinking. That held up for a while professionally. It kinda whack a-moled into my personal life though. I was drinking too much which caused problems for myself and those around me.

I only noted with mild annoyance that I had turned away a lady friend's request to spend the evening together because I was scheduled for some "proper drinking." Moments of embarrassment? Well, yeah, those too. Failure to meet commitments, or worse, showing when I should just not have.

More.

If you are reading this, just say "And..."

I went to AA, they said it was all the rage. I found it rather curious, you know, a lot with their own peculiar vernacular. I did listen a bit. I read everything they had to offer several times with marker and pen in hand. With notebook. Applied trained scholarship. I was curious about why there had been no revisions since the original message over 75 years ago. I thought I should seek some scientific help, and so I did.

A psychiatrist, who insisted he knew about alcohol abuse was my first foray into another view of treatment.

He said, "Well you are an alcoholic, you can never drink again, and if you do, you will never be able to control it. You will drink until you are jailed, hospitalized, or buried.

"Rather grim prognosis," I told him, given he had not asked me many questions.

He said, "Go to AA."

At this point, I sat puzzled. I had managed calories and such to make weight as a competitive fighter. I had measured all kinds of things to make my life better, you know mindfulness in action. I got back into Zen and sat and observed. There were some intense times I wanted a drink right there, right then...and I would excuse myself and go sit. And, notice the arising, the presence, and then the dissipation.

Well, I drank some more too much, too often, and on such the wrong occasions!

I have never liked being licked so I brought my achievement avatar out and ready for battle. I knew that observing, logging, counting, adjusting, training new, more adaptive patterns, had yielded success. in my past, across numerous endeavors. I also knew that at times when it wasn't panning out, I still suited up, showed up, and hung in there. I asked myself who was going to win "Me, or me?" I knew it was about myself. In fighting, life, weightlifting, making bonuses at work, I held agency. I knew from some lessons that I had validated, or seen validated around me, that I was going to get my behavior under control.

I created some spreadsheets and customized notebooks. I did nothing but log, Faithfully, I counted, I logged, and made notes. I went back to my background and did my own scholarship, checked sources, performed the BS test. I reviewed my logs. I started to set goals, at first big ones that didn't pan out, and I remembered that big goals had not always worked; yet incrementalism had worked and set the stage for bigger jumps.

Epiphany: I did like to drink. I did like a buzz. I knew it took more for me than others.

I started building tables, calculating everything, and I realized that if I managed my behavior, that is, drinking, I could produce the dependent variable I sought: Drink responsibly and reasonably without too much adverse health impact.

I managed schedules and parameters. Volume, timing, pacing, interval, frequency, occasion.

I missed goals along the way, always with the same reason-not observing, logging, adjusting. I re-committed and logged. I examined. I sat. I INSISTED. It got better. More insights along the way. Confidence came from looking at my logs and recognizing when it went well, or south. I had a debriefing process with myself. Non-judgmental, just understanding, learning and <u>reviewing measurements</u>.

Along the way, I wanted some sociability in my pursuits. A support group of sorts, yet oriented along the manner I was working, that *was* <u>working</u>. To share and, also, to listen, process, and learn. And, just hang out!

The day I met Moderation Management I knew I had found a group of compatriots. They had the exact attitude I had been living regarding drinking: manage the variables. I'm relatively new to MM, yet I am involved. I care about my colleagues and together we have a community to talk with, hang out. I look forward to the day we can do a cookout, a beach party, or such. Moving beyond cyberspace is much desired.

So, there it is; I have dispensed with unscientific notions and rode the wave of *the science of achievement.*

In biology, organisms first adapt, then thrive. To thrive requires a species *evolve.* That's it, I have decided, I **intend**, to eclipse myself. Adaptive behavior. As a species, we ADAPT.

<u>I have measured my nature and now I'll continue to work on conquering it.</u>

CHAPTER 4: LIVING MODERATION

From MM Member, Pierre:

I once wrote this metaphor for MM some years ago as an exercise of the English language, which is not my mother tongue, to welcome the newbies. The stages of change are out of the book "Changing for Good" from James Prochaska, a marvelous book, I recommend you to study, not only for the change of your drinking pattern, but for all changes you want to do. I want to encourage you. Since some years I am in the roof garden. It's a nice place to be. Join me! It can be done!

The House of Change

The house of change is crowded, especially the cellar which is damp, dark and cold. But the house of change has also a roof terrace where the sun is bright and life is good. The way to change goes up from the cellar to the top by means of a huge staircase. Its steps may be of variable height. The house of change has also large floors where people can rest on their way to change.

Some people in the cellar are not considering change. The are unaware that high over them there is a sunny, warm place where the view is beautiful, the air pure and the ambiance soothing. They shiver from time to time in the cold and moisture, sometimes they have a feeling that there should be a better place to be, but in the dark of the place they are in and the darkness of their mind they don't see a way to get out. They don't look for a change, maybe out of pure ignorance, well established indolence or sheer despair. They stagnate in the **stage of precontemplation***.*

There are those who stumble around in the dark, knowing that they need a change of scene, they may be driven and haunted by the memories of better days, groping about to find the latch of the exit door they know to be somewhere. Sometimes they are exhausted by the search, some give it up for good, but most are struggling and after a rest resume the search for light and a better life. They live and search in the **stage of contemplation***.*

And, suddenly, in the dark you see a small stripe of pale yellow light, almost undetectable. You stumble toward the light moved by a wild hope, you find the doorknob, you open the door and you are overwhelmed by the bright light of a staircase. On the wall sticks a poster informing you that you are now in the preparation stage and that the staircase is a magic one where you can program the height of the steps depending on your mood and ability of the present momentum. And now, you plan the first steps to take, you move on driven by your determination to advance, fleeing the dark, damp and cold cellar, up to the light. You are in the **action stage***.*

In the bright light of the large staircase, you can now see your fellow occupants the presence of who you only felt in the dark of the cellar of the house of change. They are of all races, of all continents. They are small or tall, slim or big. There are males and females of all ages, most go upstairs, some come downstairs. You are yourself melding with this community, exchanging your impressions and experiences. You are warned that you may slip downstairs, that there are some traps where

84

you can go right down to the cellar again, but always with the knowledge that there is an open door and a staircase to go up.

And so you go, up and down, but always averaging to the up, sometimes with ease, sometimes with pain. So you are passing the floors, taking a rest or not, sometimes finding yourself back on a floor where you have already been. Oh yes, this may be your fate in the action stage, but finally you reach the upper and last floor. On this floor there are club chairs where you can take a rest and meditate before opening the door to the roof terrace. You look back to your struggle, you catch a glimpse over the railing to the basement and you are proud of your journey. You are older and wiser than you were in the cellar but oh so happier. You are in the waiting room to the final stage, you are in the **_maintenance stage_**. Finally, you open the door to the roof terrace. You are in a beautiful garden, richly flowered, bees are humming, the green is greener than it was ever in your memories and dreams, the sun is brighter and the sky is bluer. You are in the **_termination stage_** and at the end of your cycle of change.

And a last bit of information. When you have opened the door leading from the cellar to the staircase, don't look for the elevator. There is no elevator in the house of change(LOL).

So many times we, as a society, grab onto the newest fad diet or exercise craze as a way to change our lives or solve our problems, and it does, for a while.

Then, the novelty wears off and we find ourselves sliding back into our old routines and established habits.

Moderating our drinking habit can also be viewed as a quick fix and it's true that following the recommended moderate drinking guidelines will result in an immediate change in our lives. However, most of us won't be able to maintain that change if our drinking routine is the only thing that changes; we will inevitably, again, slide back into our harmful drinking habits.

Successful moderation requires more of us than a desire for immediate, superficial change. Successful moderation requires an exploration of our life.

Why do we drink?

What void does drinking fill in our life?

What purpose does drinking serve?

Discovering the answers to these questions is the first step in transforming our life into a life in which we do not depend on alcohol to fill-up our empty spaces or shield us from life's stresses or uncomfortable situations. A life where alcohol plays an enjoyable but insignificant part.

Scary, huh? Some of us come to MM with the belief that solving our drinking problem will resolve all the rest of our problems when, in all actuality, alcohol has served as a barrier between us and our problems, allowing us to avoid facing and resolving them. Once the barrier is gone, we are forced to confront them.

This often serves as an excuse to keep drinking as we always have, all the while realizing we are only delaying or avoiding our problems and, in turn, delaying and avoiding the resolution of those problems. By continuing to drink as we always have, we keep ourselves stuck, unable to have the life that we really want, a life full of everything of which we are capable.

From the MM Forum's Success Story Sub-Forum:

> *"Changing our problem drinking is one of the hardest things we can face, and one of the most rewarding as well. I have never put so much work into anything in my life, and I'm very proud of the changes I've made. But that's part of what changing this habit means -- hard work. Very hard work. I discovered that this is a lifelong process. It isn't a few days of doing something different followed by a magical*

change. It's about falling down and getting back up; making plans; staying accountable; and self forgiveness."

A better, more opportune, easier time to start confronting our problems is not around the corner somewhere in the future, it is right here. The best time to start building the life we want is right now.

Moderation is not a quick fix with an expiration date or finish line, it is a new life. A life in which the weaving in of moderate tools and techniques changes not only us and the people in our life but also the landscape around us. It creates new opportunities and growth, it strengthens our faith in ourselves at the same time it strengthens others' faith in us. We finally come to know who we are and who we can be.

These changes are not by any means seamless, though. As often as we make our plans, our plans will be disrupted. As often as we think we've figured it all out, we find we have lessons yet to learn. As often as we want to give up, we realize we are too strong to surrender. As often as we fail, those failures teach us what we need to succeed.

Moderation is not the adventure of a lifetime, it *is* a lifetime.

Now, is the time to choose the lifetime we want.

The stories below are not all from people who have reached the rooftop terrace of which Pierre spoke but they are stories of people in transition, people who are climbing, people who made the choice to leave the cellar.

STORIES:

Beej's Story:

As the creator and leader of the women's weekly MM group in New York City, I've had a front-row seat to the transformation of hundreds of lives of overdrinking women as they generously share their pain, confusion, self-reflection, compassion, determination, and humor.

My own journey with overdrinking began when, after 10 years of marriage, my husband announced that he was gay, tossing me into a downward spiral. I was even diagnosed (mistakenly) with probable MS because of the panic attacks I was having which mimicked seizures.

I dealt with this shock and devastation the way I had dealt with feelings of alienation in the past—by overdrinking. Not the type of drinking that interfered with my work, but the type of drinking that made it impossible to love or care about myself. Attempts to cut down only made it worse. I was in the spin cycle.

Concerned, I mentioned it to my therapist. She actually jumped out of her chair. She told me I should go to AA. I was stunned. I felt betrayed. I just needed to talk it through with someone I trusted, to find other ways of dealing with my grief, to find ways to care for and about myself.

My solution? Quit therapy and keep overdrinking. This went on for a decade—a decade of failed relationships based on where we could find our next drink (Let's have a drink here while we're waiting for the bar to open up there, so we can drink there until it's time to go to a friend's house and drink there before returning home for a nightcap!).

I woke up one day, thought "Enough!" and started googling. I knew I couldn't possibly be the only person on the planet who had trouble cutting back but didn't fit the "alcoholic" profile.

I found Moderation Management. Through them I found a Harm Reduction Therapist. On my own I discovered Buddhism, meditation, mindfulness and somatic practices. I became a moderate drinker.

I had a passionate desire to reach back into the quicksand and pull others out, so I started the first ever MM for Women group. The coed groups were great but largely male-dominated, and women, when they did show up, usually didn't say much and would often disappear after a meeting or two. One of them, a beautiful Buddhist yoga teacher, took me aside and said "Women just...share differently." And the MM for Women's meeting was born.

Walking into the first women's meeting I was struck by the self-criticism in the room, how hard everyone was on themselves. Women seem to internalize their pain and see their struggles as indicative of some kind of personal shortcoming (unfortunately 12-Step programs can often reinforce this feeling of shame), so it came to me that

Buddhist "metta" meditation (loosely translated as Lovingkindness, or unconditional friendliness toward self) would be helpful, and I started bringing meditation instructors into the meetings.

After spending some time on my own meditation cushion and letting go of the fixed idea of who I am and what I'm capable of (up until that point I was just a professional oboe player, not that there's anything wrong with that!) it started to become clear to me that my "purpose," if you believe in such things, was to help people out of their stress and confusion and into a more easeful life, and that I was to become a mindfulness meditation instructor and life coach.

So, I started training. First as a coach (certified through NYU), then a meditation teacher (year-long Buddhist teacher training), a mindfulness teacher (years-long Mindfulness-Based Stress Reduction Teacher training), and I achieved a Certificate in Harm Reduction Psychotherapy from the New School with Dr. Andrew Tatarsky (so I could learn to work specifically with addiction).

I started to see a pattern of trauma in my coaching clients (not necessarily capital T trauma, but family, relational, childhood, and intergenerational trauma/stress) often experienced as a sense of alienation or aloneness, feeling misunderstood, unloved/unlovable, or a general sense of "something wrong with me" so I trained as a Somatic Experiencing Practitioner, working with how these feelings are held in/experienced by the body. And how to move them out.

I saw in some of my clients a stuck-ness, a sense that there was some childhood pain that needed to be healed, so I trained in hypnotherapy through the Wellness Institute.

The combination of mindfulness and somatic experiencing (and sometimes hypnosis) has proved immensely beneficial for changing patterns of behavior and emotional reactivity, and propelling people to move forward in their lives.

Which brings us back to the drinking, which so often is based in anxiety, in difficulty handling emotions, and then becomes habitual!

What I love about the MM philosophy is that it gives you agency. You get to decide what feels right to you— There are suggested guidelines, but no strict limits.

Limits often feel—well—limiting— and confining, so people often rebel and give up.

MM members get to voice their concerns in a gentle, forgiving, nonjudgmental atmosphere. They get to try out things and discover what works and what doesn't work for them. (After all, we are all individuals with our own unique set of conditioning and experiences.) We share tools and techniques, but with the understanding that what works for one person won't automatically work for another. We celebrate triumphs and offer encouragement when things don't go as planned. We laugh. We cry. We experience what it is to be human, together.

Beej Christie Karpen
Certified Coach; Mindfulness-Based Stress Reduction Teacher
Insight Out Mindfulness Coaching & Hypnotherapy For Problem Drinking
http://www.insightoutnyc.com/
https://www.psychologytoday.com/profile/303126

Nils' Story: Milestones on the Road to Onesies

In my time at MM, I've observed that people decide to address their drinking habits for a variety of sound reasons. For me it wasn't the hangovers, which I'd always considered a fair part of the price to pay. Nor was it the cycle of anxiety, although heaven knows I'm glad to have broken free of it. It wasn't even concern over my health, which largely came later, once I started to listen to the warnings my body was sending me. Rather, my main motivation was a growing resentment of the time I was spending drinking or recovering from drinking.

Compared to many of my peers, I was a latecomer to alcohol, only really getting started during my time at university. I seemed determined to make up for lost time though and, finding that it provided me with a way past my shyness, I would seize any opportunity to fritter away the days in pubs and bars. This pattern continued and intensified after I graduated. Throughout my 20s, my diet would generally consist of around 8-10 drinks a night, more at weekends, along with the unhealthy food choices that go hand in hand with such a lifestyle. I would often spend the whole day in the pub, reading the newspaper and drinking with others who would come and go. From time to time, it occurred to me that these people were engaging in other activities during the rest of their days, but I wasn't yet ready to join them. During my late 20's and 30's, I did make the occasional lacklustre attempt to reduce my drinking, most notably after a blood pressure scare which ultimately just added an appreciation of red wine into the equation.

It was in my early 40s that the feeling I was continuing to waste so much precious time really started to bother me to the extent that I resolved to do something about it. I'd done a hundred-day period of abstinence with some friends which I hadn't found too challenging, despite my previous habits, but I didn't want to adopt that lifestyle full time, so I set myself some limits that I sketchily followed. Even then it was a half-hearted effort and although I managed to reduce my daily drinking, I lacked the commitment or focus to make any real progress and frequently exceeded my self-imposed limits. That was when I discovered Moderation Management. I joined MM early in 2013, did a 30, started recording my drinks on Abstar and, then, like so many people do, drifted off and alarmingly quickly returned to many of my old habits.

I continued to observe abstinence days though, as well as logging my drinks so at the start of 2015, nine months after taking early retirement and feeling that I wasn't fully appreciating the opportunity I'd given myself, I was finally ready and able to analyze exactly where I stood and to get serious about tackling my issues. I made what proved to be a landmark MM forum post for me, where I observed that, during the previous year, on 7 out of every 10 days when I drank, I went on to overdrink, often into double figures. This was despite over a third of my days being abstinent, including what was by then an annual dry month, so it was clear to me that non-drinking days were at least one aspect in which I had already made some progress. I made a conscious effort therefore to focus on achieving more moderate drinking days, practicing various techniques for stopping after the requisite number of drinks and building my commitment to extending my periods of success at doing so.

I managed streaks of up to a month or two of successful moderation, punctuated by periods when I sometimes struggled to regain traction but always felt that I was now committed to this path and I would get back to it with renewed vigour. Gradually, the periods of moderation grew longer and the times between shorter and less severe and I realized that what was motivating me most was setting milestone targets, working towards them and ticking them off. So, with the help of MM admin, we established an area on the forum for members to do just that and to record when they achieve those milestones, for their own and others' benefit. Posting my progress after first a month, then 3 months, 6 months, a year and, then, 2 years of unbroken By-The-Book moderation gave me huge satisfaction and allowed me each time to look back on my experience and tweak my plan accordingly.

During that first full year of BTB, my primary focus was simply to remain within the moderation guidelines at all times. When I reviewed my situation at the end of it, I found that I felt happier when I routinely stuck to a single drink, reserving second or third drinks for special, planned occasions (I'm male, but for closer alignment with the current UK alcohol guidelines I observe the MM recommended limit for females of three drinks per occasion as well as at least 3 days of abstinence per week). This approach gradually evolved to the point where I limited even planned events to two drinks and then progressed quite organically to where I've found myself for the last 6 months: happily sticking to a single "real-world" drink (aka a "onesie") on all occasions.

It's not cast in stone and it's not for everyone but personally I'm prepared to sacrifice flexibility and spontaneity for stability and there's no denying that this strategy addresses the issue that brought me to MM: I no longer waste time drinking or recovering from drinking.

These days I appreciate the few drinks I have rather than mourning the ones I've "lost". I sometimes get wistful for those all-day sessions of untrammelled drinking in convivial, sunlit pubs but I recognise that for what it is: an idealised memory that disregards the costs of that lifestyle, a price I'm no longer willing to pay.

<u>Hope L.'s Story</u>: Finding My Other Half

Rediscovering the part of me that got left behind while drinking.

I was always worried about being left behind as a child. Overlooked by the neighborhood kids during summer tag games, left off the list for high school party invites. Even as an adult, accomplished in my field, when a smooth-talking heavy hitter turns away from me mid-sentence for someone deemed more worthy, that same feeling is there. I'm not good enough.

This is a story about realizing, through flirting with sobriety, that I had lost a beautiful part of myself years ago and then suddenly began to find myself again. The person I thought I was going to be when I grew up, somewhere along the way disappeared into the void. This story is about a girl that was told over and over again that she wasn't terribly pretty, her ideas were too loud, and she wasn't very smart or terribly talented. Just. Not. Enough. I have spent the past year plus of my journey reaching back and grabbing onto the hand of that small girl, talking to her late at night, crying during a yoga class with her, bringing her back to where she belongs. This is her story, and possibly yours.

Finding the drink.

When I started this journey of learning about how alcohol somehow became a big, fat hairy major part of my life, I had my story neatly packaged up in my mind. The problem had started in college, and had gotten worse when I met my husband in my early twenties while working in bars and restaurants. Easy access to parties, and spontaneous fun, all revolving around drinking. Then out of nowhere a shared memory from a friend on social media told a very different story. Her version of my story placed me square in the middle of starting to drink way earlier than I'd been telling myself.

Mind blown.

This memory jolt felt like a physical shredding of the wiring inside my head, making me feel unsteady about my very existence. I knew drinking had robbed me of many lost moments, ranging from time with my kids to watching a movie five times over the last few years and not knowing the ending, but now I saw this demon had also physically changed my brain and the way it functions.

The gates were now open. Other pieces of my past came back into focus. Painful relationship issues from the past I'd buried and "gotten over" crept back in without invitation, situations I'd completely forgotten started to resurface for a second look. The clarity of new sobriety offered a safe passage back in time to see those moments for what they were. To make peace with them. This realization that the person I thought I was all these years may actually be quite different than what I'd been carrying around, this is when things got really serious with my drinking journey.

I hadn't planned for this part. I had been focused on the physical benefits of moderation and sobriety, immersed in all sorts of quit lit and online support groups and pouring my heart out in a private online journal.

Until then I felt sorta kinda in control of the journey. But now I felt like I was wrestling a giant bear that had moved into my house that nobody else could see but me.

Things fall apart.

More began to unravel in my life, some within my control and some not. I started to wonder if I'd not been paying attention and this all had been happening all along, or if cutting back on the booze allowed this new lens of clarity. Soon enough, I found out this was the first step towards finding my old self again.

There she is.

I didn't recognize her at first, the old me, which sounds ridiculous when I say it out loud. I started looking for her, in photos and old clothes, dusty boxes and dysfunctional friendships. I was able to slow down and watch clouds float by or read a book before bed with her. She slowly started to come around more often and walk alongside me. I felt like I was carrying a big secret around, that everyone around me was going about their lives, happy as clams, and I had somehow moved into this alternative universe of reality, almost like I had an imaginary friend. But it felt, well, good.

Feeling good, I realized, was something I'd been lacking for a while. Good about me.

This young girl, full of dreams and hope was back in my life. She was skinny, hungry and unsure. I barely recognized her, as it had been so long since we'd seen each other. We hung out together, writing each morning, sharing our secrets and guzzling seltzer and ginger beer, becoming someone who took baths and went to bed early without apology. We are still getting to know each other again, she and I. She is still so very young and full of the blissful optimism that youth offers, which sometimes feels uncomfortable and hard to me. But she's teaching me how to give in and retrieve parts of me that were so important back then, parts that went missing. I've rekindled a special friendship with an old and dear friend I ignored for decades, someone I blew off, kicked around and shut out of my life, and she's forgiven me for all of it. Strangely enough that feeling I've always had of never being good enough, or being left behind isn't there anymore. I've got myself back.

Hope L. at http://www.backpocketsobriety.com/

MM Member's Story: Success In Progress

It's safe to say that alcoholism runs in the family. My father drank daily for most of his life. He quit in his mid–forties when I was already going to college and off to the big city so I really never had the chance to get to know his sober version—I was always afraid of him. I still am to a degree even though he passed away 4 years ago.

The memories from my childhood kept me away from alcohol even through college. My drinking began around 2005 when I moved to my first apartment, one I didn't share with anyone else, I mean. In a way, I always drank socially but it wasn't my thing. I used to go to clubs a lot, but I was always more interested in the music rather than the booze.

It has to be that when you're past 30 you start going out to drink more and catch up with friends and the alcohol bar (not the place!) is raised. It was around that time that I decided I was going to "learn to drink", I started having terrible hangovers. It was either that or puking at people's places, I told myself. And, I had this awesome apartment and why not have one of those minibars too, "let's make this into a decent bachelor's pad," I thought.

So, I started buying hard liquor and I was really enjoying having Friday nights by myself, watching a movie (movies, books, and music are my thing) and having some new drinks.

I managed to keep this moderation with booze for a couple of years but around 2007 I was having problems at work and started feeling not so good about my career. I had been working since 2000 for this TV company in the technology area and felt pretty stuck. My boss at the time was having an affair with a co-worker that was younger than me and she would probably get the promotion for which I'd been on the lookout for a while. My personal life wasn't that great either. I'd lost touch with my friends. The drinking escalated to a bottle of wine every day and a bottle or two of vodka on the weekends.

At some point, I left that job for one that paid much better, but it was equally stressful. In short, for the next 7 years, I had a stretch of really shitty jobs and I didn't know how to say "NO!" to my managers. I spent 7 years without a single day off.

In 2010 I found myself in a C-level position for a medium-sized agency. I was so burnt out that, when I realized they wouldn't give me any vacation time after a year there, I quit and took a job that paid half but had vacations as a benefit. I needed to stop for a while and, in my head, it was always the job, never my drinking, that was the problem. I wasn't like my father, how could I be? I didn't get as cranky as he did when he was drunk, I was a happy chatty drunk, so I was ok.

My plan was to take this job, take a month off and find something else in the ballpark that I was used to making moneywise. I had no problems finding interviews. In fact, recruiters were getting in touch and I was getting some interesting contacts and being interviewed twice every other week.

I just couldn't land a proposal, no matter what. These companies wouldn't touch me with a ten-foot pole. I wasn't drinking in the mornings then (yet!). I don't think I reeked of alcohol.

In hindsight, I think I was sending out these SOS signals and people were catching them and, rightly so, not wanting to have anything to do with me.

That broke me, really. My drinking binges started to extend past the weekends. I would call in sick and not show up until Wednesday at least once a month. I would not drink on Thursdays but Fridays, come on: I've managed to go through this week, I deserve to drink. I wouldn't even care about watching movies with a drink. It was all about the drink.

Then, the company I was working for started to show signs of bankruptcy, just my luck. They started laying people off. I was in a panic. This was 2013 and was probably around the time I started to look for help and found MM. I don't really remember how because it was probably on a Monday that I called in sick so I could keep on drinking.

How many times I went through all the Listserv emails with my hands shaking from the night before! It took me about a year to write my first post. It was after one of my worst weeks, the first one I had to call in sick for the whole week. It was also the week I started to go to therapy sessions. This was my lowest, I never really thought I would have suicidal thoughts, that really scared me.

It was a couple of months to the day when I decided to "stick" (abstain from alcohol in MM lingo) for a weekend. Damn, that was hard. I wrote an email to the list for accountability and a few others over Saturday and Sunday. It was a success and I had the first Monday with no hangover in years, but I wouldn't repeat that for a long time. My therapy sessions were on Mondays and I started experimenting with the amounts of alcohol I could have in order to show up. I zeroed in on one bottle on Sundays, a limit I kept for a while. It felt like progress, somewhat.

Things took a wrong turn when my father died later that year. He had been cancer free for 7+ years but, in a rare twist, it came back again in all its pancreatic glory. I don't think I reverted back to what I was drinking before but I was calling in sick often enough to make the next layoff list.

To be honest, that was the best thing that could have happened to me. I inherited some money and took half a year off. I started to exercise every day, started to do more stickies and F'abs and trikes (4 and 3 days of abstinence in a week, again in MM lingo).

I started to walk straight—it occurred to me while I was walking my dog that I was seeing things at a different angle because I had changed my posture! Was it because I wasn't hungover all the time and henceforth not feeling guilty? Was it the absence of pressure from not being in a job I hated, in a company that was sinking? Probably a bit of all.

After a lot of thought, I decided I would only work remotely and moved back to my hometown. My therapist was against this, but I thought things would be different now that my father was gone.

And it was, in a way. I've been living here for 4 years now and in these four years I've had a lot of ups and downs and a few binges but I decided to experiment on trying to find the right dosage for me because I just love drinking a good wine while watching a movie or finishing a book and I don't want to give that up. What I found out is, that by abstaining a few days in a week, I get to enjoy more of those times. In my "bad years" I spent three years without finishing a book. Anyone who knows me would know how crazy that is. I just couldn't think of anything but drinking.

With help from MM, therapy, and a lot of trial and error, I decided to not drink on weekdays. I got a job at one of the 100 most innovative technology companies (or so they say about us) three years ago and I love it, albeit it's super demanding, as it should be. Now, I feel that even one glass of wine the night before really takes its toll on me. So, I've managed to only drink on Saturdays and Sundays. And, guess what? Sometimes binges still happen, but not more than twice or three times a year in these last 4 years.

Two years ago, I did my first 30 (30 days in a row abstaining from alcohol). It was hard, just like my first weekend abstaining in 2014, but it got easier and, to be honest, I can't recall how many 30s I've done since then – 5 or 6ish, maybe. I've found that I don't want to give up alcohol for now and, also, that I'm not a stellar moderator, but the scheme I have right now kind of works for me.

Andre's Story: To Stay the Course

"Perfect is the enemy of the good."

The above quote — commonly attributed to Voltaire — is a pretty common refrain in our local face-to-face meeting. Perhaps someone didn't quite complete their Thirty, or had four drinks at an event where they planned to have only three. The quote puts things in clear perspective: "Four months ago you couldn't string three abstaining days together, but you just completed three dry weeks. Last year you might have had eight drinks at that same party; last weekend, you had half that amount." In other words, let's acknowledge and celebrate our significant improvements even while regretting our occasional shortcomings.

When I began this journey over six years ago, I was like a frightened deer in the headlights. A relationship had just fallen apart, due in no small part to my copious beer consumption. My abuse of alcohol was at least familiar, a tiresome ritual; but complete, lifelong abstinence didn't seem very appealing at that moment. Certainly, there had to be another way, a third path between continued misuse and total abstinence. I typed a few keywords in the search engine and began the process that has led me here today (commencing with a six-month spell of total abstinence, which I then felt was a crucial step).

The early days were exhausting. After my beer-soaked brain had dried up a little, my thoughts were completely preoccupied — not so much with drinking, but with *not* drinking. How would I chart a course through this new life, when the old life was barely in my rearview mirror? A lot of contemplative walks and too many cans of Red Bull, but I knew I had to be patient: this may not happen overnight, but it will happen if I stick with it and believe in myself.

During that six months of abstinence, I felt a new person gradually emerge. I was still tethered to my old identity, but I began to be more patient with myself, less worried about the future, more confident with my interior strength. I read a lot on the subject of addiction (the "A word" I'm still most comfortable with) and learned something of the science behind our hijacked brains and the powerful forces of habit. I haunted online forums and message boards. And an important revelation came to me: *that every single drink in my life had been a willful, voluntary act.* I had learned this maladaptive behavior, and I could unlearn it as well. I began attending weekly Moderation Management meetings, where I met so many interesting people going through similar struggles — sometimes expressing sorrow and trauma, but also a lot of laughter accompanied by knowing nods and grins. I initially participated to help myself, but over time learned that helping others is even more rewarding.

Has it been one long victory lap? Of course not. The old adage of "two steps forward, one step back" has never been more apropos. I've stumbled a few times (both literally and figuratively) but somehow have always managed to correct the course. I used to carry so much guilt and shame during the bad old days, and it's been wonderful to feel that burden lifted off my chest. I occasionally wince remembering the things I used to do but have largely forgiven myself. What's most important to me now is the continuing goal of a *"sustainable peace"* — maybe not by-the-book perfection all the time, but something I can live with at the end of the day. Additionally, it's important to actually *enjoy* the glass of wine or dram of scotch — I don't want to find myself tortured in a constant state of self-recrimination and self-flagellation. (Americans have had such a conflicted, unhealthy relationship with alcohol for far too long, dating back to our Puritan forefathers, through Prohibition, and now in today's hyper-saturated marketing of booze as a glamorous 'lifestyle' product. As a society, we really need to grow up a little.)

Returning to the opening quote: it's so easy to get frustrated and throw in the towel when things don't work out as planned. But progress is progress, and better is better. We need to forgive ourselves for our occasional failings and keep our healthy goals in sight. And, wherever possible, it's so helpful to talk about this part of our lives to others—strangers, friends, or family, many of who are struggling with their own issues as well. Alcohol misuse is now broadly recognized as a spectrum disorder, with individuals existing in different bands of the spectrum. Pursuit of perfection is fine — but let's not let it get in the way of making some meaningful changes right now.

MM Member's Story: **Don't Stop Searching Before You Find Your Solution (Sinclair Method)**

My success with moderation took me by surprise and I'm amazed by it every day. I tried and failed for 10 years to moderate after a 25-year drinking career, one that started as excellent fun and ended with me hovering just above the gutter. I was a functional alcoholic, barely managing to keep things together enough to not get fired, which was insanely exhausting (insane being an apt word).

I fell in love with alcohol the moment I had my first buzz at 14. I'd been terrified of drinking after my father landed in the literal gutter, with alcohol destroying not only his charm but turning him into a thief and a liar (a homeless one at that). But my fear faded a few moments after I took a shot of Bacardi and relaxed and felt comfortable in my body for the first time in my life. Alcohol became my everything. A friend felt the same –

and we sought it out every weekend and had a blast doing so.

Alcohol stayed my closest friend for nearly 20 years – through college, relationships, friendships, jobs, but it turned on me when I was 33. I started to black out regularly, drinking morning, noon, and night. I started to isolate, drank at work, had sex with people I don't remember, ruined friendships and relationships, went into deep debt, ended up in the hospital with DTs, made an utter fool of myself more times than I can count, and, after several years fighting it, finally crawled into AA. After a few hits and misses, I stayed. Leading up to it, I struggled in every way I knew to try and drink normally; willpower, books on moderation, Naltrexone, vitamin concoctions, planning nights in advance, etc and etc. Nothing worked.

In AA, I did what they told me. Ninety meetings in 90 days. Sponsors. Steps. But I dreaded every meeting. I did make it 14 months, but then dove back into drinking.

My return to alcohol was a little better than how I left it (with some expensive exceptions – like when I woke up with a $300 cab receipt and checked my phone records to realize that on my way home from a business trip in DC, I had taken a cab from Philadelphia to New York City because I got confused at the train station – they are both named Penn Station and I got off at the wrong one; my neighbors told me the cops brought me home because I couldn't remember my address so the cab driver took me to the one on my license). Yet I still managed to keep my job and somehow forge an amazing relationship with the man who is now my husband. But things got to a point (see above for an example) where I agreed to stop again. This relationship was more important to me than my relationship with alcohol.

Depression set in again – the thought of meetings and the emptiness they made me feel was terrifying. I should say I'm incredibly thankful AA exists and has helped so many people, including my father who was sober the last 25 years of his life. But it wasn't for me. I went to another meeting but left halfway though and went to a bar. Certainly, a bad move when an engagement is on the line. I promised to get help though, one way or another. I found the Sinclair Method online. It involved Naltrexone, which I'd tried before unsuccessfully, but with the Sinclair method you take it an hour before you drink, and only on the days you drink. I read everything I could find about it and watched a movie called "*One Little Pill*" with my fiancé. I was extremely skeptical. I knew myself and my brain and my family's tendency towards drugs and alcohol (my father and I weren't the only ones).

I asked my doctor about Naltrexone, for the first time admitting to him that I had a problem, and he immediately dropped me as a patient. He didn't want the liability of an addict.

I found another doctor who helps people with moderation and addiction and thankfully she took my insurance. I started right away and the change was immediate and world changing. My drinking cut down by half, I didn't have cravings, and I didn't wake up thinking about alcohol. I wouldn't have believed it possible if it didn't happen to me.

I also found a therapist/life coach who runs the Moderation Management women's group in NYC. And, I joined the C Three Foundation (https://cthreefoundation.org/), which offers support to people on the Sinclair Method (or TSM) and found a wonderful online community who share their stories.

I'm far from cured, and I still have days where I drink too much. But I've had maybe three hangovers in the last year and a half. Before I would have had three in any given three days.

Why would I still want a relationship with something that's been so destructive? I cannot answer that. We are irrational beings. But, thankfully, by what seems to be a miracle, it's now a healthy relationship. Now I can work on the 'why' to the question above with a clear head.

I am amazed this treatment isn't more popular. There is still a mentality that addicts are just wastes that need to fix themselves. And there's the mentality in the recovery community that only AA can work. It can and does, but there are now other ways.

I also know people moderate without medication, including my therapist. That is amazing to me, and more power to them. It didn't work for me, but humans react to things differently. We are all case studies.

I am eager to help spread the word about these treatments. Too many people are needlessly suffering and dying, and science can help them. I hope my story gets to people in need.

Kira's Story:

International Travel without drinking? Yes, it can be done.

I'm in my first year of moderation, 9 months to be exact. I went nine months with minimal (okay non-existent) drinking exactly two times before in my adult life: when I was pregnant with my daughter, and then 3 years later, with my son. They're now 20 and 17 respectively. Since my 20's, my drinking has grown slowly but steadily from social situations and occasional wine at home with my husband to habitual closet drinking on my own.

When my daughter was a kindergartner, we loved to go to the local playground. We'd spend hours running around, carefree and laughing. There was a small, walled-in spot on the jungle gym, where she would force me to contort my adult body behind a minuscule table so that we could play "restaurant." She would pretend to take out her pad and would politely ask what I wanted. She'd scribble down the order, go fetch some pine needles and leaves, and I'd act like they were the most delicious meal I ever pretend-ate.

One day, my back was hurting a bit and I suggested that I be the server and she be the customer. When I asked for her order, she exclaimed without any hesitation "I'll have a salad and WINE!" Wow. I should have seen the warning signs then, but I laughed uproariously, went home and related the tale to my husband, family, friends, and anyone else who would listen. After all, I only ever drink wine and beer; how could I possibly have a drinking problem?

Fast forward: I find myself on an international flight to Singapore with said daughter – preparing to leave her there for 4.5 months for a semester abroad. We have a solid relationship and we had several glasses of champagne together on the way over. It was an 18-hour flight with a connection, so it was a way to pass the time. Never mind the inevitable headache that comes with in-flight drinking, it's just a foregone conclusion that airline travel includes alcohol, right? On the way home alone, I had another several glasses of wine, again to pass the time, but also to drown out the emotions of leaving my now very scared daughter who begged me not to leave.

Well, we got many tearful phone calls in that first month and my husband and I finally broke and agreed to two separate trips to visit her. His would tandem with work, mine would just be for pleasure. But I had also just started Moderation Management and seeing a therapist. My drinking had gone way beyond acceptable and it was time to get my shit together.

How to face those excruciatingly boring 18 hours each way without my favorite crutch? It was a daunting idea. I don't react well to change, and I knew it was going to be altogether too easy to cheat since I would be alone. After all, who would ever know?

I needed a plan, and a rock solid one. Through therapy, and a lot of reading, I knew that I aspire to receive love in the form of acknowledgment, specifically words of affirmation.

Nothing makes my day like a good compliment. It was important that people understand what I was about to attempt, so that I could bring them on as cheerleaders.

First off, I made sure my therapist and my husband would be available by text during much of my flight. I bought in-flight wifi access for the first time ever. I've never been willing to justify it before, but this ensured two cheerleaders for a mere $40 - a pittance compared to my previous monthly wine bills! (Turned out, we flew up and over the north pole and we only had wifi access for about 5 of the 18 hours - so much for those $40! - but they were with me at the beginning and end of the flight, enough to give me lots of encouragement.)

I then introduced myself to my flight attendant - an adorable, young Indonesian man named Cody. I'll never forget him. "Cody," I said, "I need to confide in you. I'm newly sober and I really want to make it through this flight without drinking. I'm hoping by telling you this, I will feel accountability and not ask you for any wine." Without blinking an eye he replied, "Don't you worry, we're going to get through this together!"

Over the next many hours, he was attentive without being overbearing. He gave me a thumbs up when I asked him to prepare herbal tea I had brought with me and he kept glasses of water at the ready. At the end of the flight, I gave him a huge hug, and he hugged right back and told me he was proud of me. I arrived in Asia rested, alert and with no headache for the first time - I had done it! What a sense of accomplishment.

Since then, I've done several more flights, all sober. In fact, I'm writing this on a flight from New York to San Francisco, with my trusty tea tumbler sitting next to me.

I'm heading to Tahoe to do a Century bike ride around the lake (100 miles) for charity. I still have my bad days, and fight with myself and my demons. But I'm committed and I'm learning to equip myself with successful strategies that work with my love language of affirmation. Knowing what makes your heart full is powerful, it makes you stronger and more able to look your urges in the eye and say, "I'm worth so much more than that glass of alcohol."

Katy's Story: Alcohol – To Drink or Not to Drink?

Stopping an addiction like drinking, or moderating the habit, is an ongoing debate in some circles. Whether to quit or regulate?

Alcoholics Anonymous says that drinkers are "powerless" over alcohol and need to "turn it over to a higher power." Moderation Management offers a place to empower yourself – that is, to manage it.

For me, the MM program is about self-empowerment. It's not always easy but it gives people choices (everything from abstinence to having two drinks a day or just on weekends, etc.) and time to find their own way.

In *Moderation Management*, members have different reasons for drinking. Some want the "buzz", some are driven by fear of dealing with daily tasks of living or need help with social anxiety. Some people want to numb old trauma and memory- reasons to drink range widely and wildly.

In our society, we live with a speedy pace of life that is stressful. (Not to mention politics in the country making us all bite our nails.) So, we turn to habits to deal with our hungers, our loneliness, deaden sorrow, deal with depression, get happy and so on.

I have found through the years of struggling with my own addictions including serial romantic love partners, quitting cigarettes, losing 100 pounds (compulsive overeating) or moderating my drinking- that different approaches have worked for me, and some approaches – not so much.

In Moderation Management, I am finding that a lot of people discuss: "Why would I drink too much when it makes me more stupid and upsets my digestion?" Increasingly MM seems to include dialogues about how to change our behaviors, but also what is at the bottom of such self-harm?

Triggers that can cause us to numb or cheer ourselves are everywhere – from relationship break ups to aggressive bosses at work. A lot of us long for something to hold onto, to feel filled up, to lessen fear and help us feel calm or socialize or have sex and so on.

I'm just saying there's another way, besides A.A. But, Bill W. and A.A. changed the world for many and I've found each path helpful.

We all have to find our own way to wellness.

My family history and the culture said, "AA is the only way," but, in MM I see that there is no absolute rule. Some people quit drinking without AA, some replace alcohol with marijuana, some go back to AA and many eventually regulate their habits. But whichever way you go, you have tools for change, like delaying the drink or planning the evening or breathing into the social anxiety instead of gulping something.

In studying alternatives to AA, I found "Over the Influence", by Denning, Little and Glickman (https://www.amazon.com/dp/B073D9XKR4/). The book says that women can feel especially disempowered by the idea that they cannot manage their own lives or by lying to themselves about their overuse. Helplessness is not an idea that is emphasized in MM. The book states: "There is surprisingly little actual denial on the part of people who use alcohol and other drugs. Every time a drinker is confronted about her use of alcohol, she feels it. She may be lying, minimizing the problem, ambivalent, hopeful that she can make it better, hopeless about doing anything different, or fearful about losing that warm blanket that alcohol wraps around her each evening, but she's not in denial.... Since we believe that many drug users have already been traumatized and badly shamed, we find the idea of breaking someone's spirit in this way to be horrifying. ...Powerlessness is a difficult concept. It is questionable, especially for women who have been in a less than powerful position in society for so long."

AA is a profoundly important way to go. It began with pioneering and divine intervention that has saved many lives. The Twelve Step Programs worldwide help multitudes of people. However, some people struggle with the Twelve Steps or feel they do not need/want to quit drinking completely, and, those people need support also.

Other reading, about moderating your drinking, includes "*Responsible Drinking*," by Rotgers, Kern and

Hoeltzel, along the lines of moderating alcohol consumption reads like this: "I have never sunk back to the drinking levels of those earlier years... I do have a few rules that I can follow that really seem to help. I don't start drinking past a certain hour.... I never drink on an empty stomach. I keep track. Drink water. Listen to your body etc. ...think substitution not restriction."

For me, delaying my drinking and planning it have been life- saving and healthy. It is a process and a responsibility to find what works for you. I now enjoy socializing with wine and function all day long.

But, the internal wounds are a worthy opponent. This is an ongoing process. We may be sensitive people. I am grateful that I now know my triggers and how to manage my responses and self soothe.

Whether I struggle with french fries at midnight or anxiety – I am glad there are alternative ways to recover from these life- sucking habits.

Katy Byrne, MA, MFT Psychotherapist
Author of "The Courage to Speak Up",
katybyrne.com,
707 548 8982.

18490 Riverside Dr., Sonoma, Ca. 95476

G. S. Hunter's Story: Journey of a Thousand Steps

In July of 2015, I retired from the US Air Force after 24 years of service and having done nothing else since age 17. At the same point, I had been married 18 years to my best friend. Putting aside such a big slice of my identity was terrifying and intimidating, and, while I longed to begin a new voyage of self-discovery, I found myself losing the fight against negative emotions and depression. What had been a simple "one drink every couple days" enjoyable habit became "half a bottle every night." Compounding this poor choice of coping was the stress to my marriage from retirement, suddenly being home after two decades more often apart, and my increased drinking. Self-feeding cycle? Yes, yes indeed.

What began as poor coping with a single life change thus led to multiple parts of my life falling away from me. At some point, the inevitability of the end of my marriage settled in and I resolved that, if I were to move ahead alone, I wanted the company to be worth keeping. As such, and with the aid of my therapist, I found Moderation Management, and, in so doing, found a wellspring of support that I'd not imagined. I knew while it was entirely feasible for me to lose myself in a bottle for the rest of my life that was not who I wanted my new self to be. And in resolving to learn about myself, I realized I needed to learn about the unaltered me and so needed to control the drinking.

MM was a wondrous addition to my toolbox – I found a community of like-minded people, supportive and honest, equally forthcoming with their successes...and failures. I found tools to help hold myself accountable through ABSTAR and monthly challenges. Most of all, I found I was not alone. I had KNOWN it, but logic and feelings are often quite separate from each other. The warm welcome I got upon registering and the sense of kinship in reading the stories and tribulations of others, quieted those feelings of being alone and let me leverage my logical mind to see a gradual path forward.

In addition, and especially key for me after a lifelong career of service, I found I could help others as well – a simple word of encouragement, an "I know what you are saying," inviting others into abstinence and moderation challenges – all let me feel like a contributing member of the community. Getting messages back expressing appreciation was the best feeling of all – not only was I not alone, but I was helping others to feel the same way.

We all take steps back. We have an off night, or an off week. ABSTAR paints a frustrating picture of control lost along the way. And yet, the community rallies with everyone, picks them up and dusts them off (or even picks them up and carries them along until they can walk on their own again) and people are renewed. No one is shamed, no one is made to feel lesser and all receive genuine encouragement.

MM is what a support community and resource is meant to be, and I think the success stories people tell speak highly to that. It is entirely possible that I might have eventually pulled myself out of the bottle and forced myself to change, but there was no guarantee. My success story is not my own, but rather the combined efforts, care and generosity of the MM community. Truly, this journey is unending, and of the thousand steps forward, I know I will take many backward steps and even fall from time to time. But I also know that I have friends there who will help me back up and continue to move ahead.

The band Disturbed has a song out on their Evolution album called "A Reason To Fight." To me, this is MM expressed lyrically and musically, and I encourage others to listen to it and take it to heart. Comradeship and teamwork has defined much of my life, and MM has continued that for me. I can freely say I am a better man, better able to deal with the perils and pitfalls of life, and better equipped to strike out into this new chapter of my existence thanks to this group of amazing people.

"When the demons come again, call to me, my brother, and we shall fight them together."

CHAPTER 5: THE CHOICE OF ABSTINENCE

One obstacle that keeps many of us from reaching out for support when we first feel our control over alcohol slipping, is the fear that abstinence, for the rest of our lives, is the option that will be forced on us. Abstinence has come to signify a desperate "last option." Add in the "forever" commitment that has been tagged onto it, and it becomes an option that anyone who has ever enjoyed an alcoholic beverage avoids as if it were a death sentence.

Certainly, none of us that found our way to MM were ready to entertain the thought of abstinence forever, or for even the indefinite future. We would give moderation everything we had before accepting that abstinence was the only choice left to us, that's what we promised ourselves.

But, then again, most of us had not experienced an abstinent period of significant length in a long time, or ever, in our adulthood. It is with astonishment that we discover, in introducing abstinent periods into our moderation routine, that there is a freedom and simplicity to abstinence that we enjoy. Who knew we would find ourselves looking forward to breaks from drinking and the attentiveness that moderation requires? That the predictability of abstinence would become a welcome respite from the variability of moderation, especially during stressful periods in our lives.

Although some members continue to view abstinence as their final option if moderation is not successful or maintainable for them, others choose the newly discovered stability and serenity of abstinence willingly. In abstinence, they find a freedom they haven't experienced in a long time, if ever. These members often express regret that because of their fear of being forced or coerced into abstinence, they delayed the extraordinary path that was waiting for them. They admit, though, that it was their path through moderation that lead them to where they belonged and if moderation had not been an option, they may never have gotten there.

Abstinence is extremely empowering when given the chance to be embraced and chosen freely instead of forced or accepted in acquiescence.

As always, MM supports our members in making the choice *they* as individuals perceive to be the right path for themselves. The decision to abstain from alcohol permanently or for an indefinite period is not seen as failure or lack of commitment to moderation. Instead, it is celebrated as a milestone decision for the member who makes this choice. Members who decide to pursue abstinence continue to be welcome in our community and are encouraged to share their experiences. Our own MMabsers subgroup is a close-knit community that offers support and guidance for anyone choosing abstinence for any amount of time. (https://groups.yahoo.com/neo/groups/mmabsers/info)

MMabsers also welcomes members of other abstinence-based support programs including:
Alcoholic Anonymous (https://www.aa.org/),
SMART Recovery (https://www.smartrecovery.org/),
LifeRing (https://www.lifering.org/),
And Women For Sobriety (https://womenforsobriety.org/).

STORIES

Ruth Marie's Story:

Prior to joining Moderation Management, I had been a daily drinker for 25 years, occasionally moderate, usually not. When I joined the MM forum in April, 2016, my total number of drinks for the month was 150, and abstinent (abs) days totaled zero. I had no intention of abstinence – ever! But it was obvious I needed to cut back. The biggest challenge in following the moderate drinking guidelines was incorporating abs days, and it took me a while to build up the courage to attempt that first one. (Side note: it did not literally kill me.)

Over time, I was able to reduce my intake significantly thanks to the unconditional support and encouragement of the fine people in the group. The path was by no means smooth and straight. I stumbled many a time but kept getting back up. Both the group and the Abstar feature kept me accountable and motivated to keep trying. I immersed myself in books, podcasts, and sober blogs and found them inspiring with regard to living alcohol free, but never even considered that as a goal. I had hoped that reducing the fluid ounces would diminish the importance of alcohol in my life, but I think it had the opposite effect.

Even when successfully moderating and abstaining, I was using an inordinate amount of brain space obsessing about drinking/not drinking.

I grew to enjoy how I felt during extended periods of abstinence such as Dryuary, but once I started drinking again a constant, mild anxiety about the whole business seemed to cloud my every waking hour. I would feel crappy and "forget" how great it felt when I didn't drink. Plus, if I had more than two, I felt much worse the next day than usual -- maybe it was my age (61) and/or tolerance changing, but I think much of that was driven by guilt and disappointment in myself. I finally had to admit that I felt better and life simply seemed easier when I didn't drink at all. So, I invented challenges of 60, 90, and 100 days. I would usually get about 75% completed before reverting to old habits, then realize I was miserable and start over again.

In April 2018, I had an embarrassing event that involved chugging cheap boxed wine for no occasion at all... just because it was there and no one was looking. I got sick and was humiliated as my very kind and patient husband cleaned up and got me tucked into bed. I fell asleep/passed out thinking, "That's it. I'm done."

The next day I felt ashamed but also excited about my decision. I re-started my sobriety counter at Day One (for the 17th time, ha!) I use the **NoMo sobriety counter app**, and as of this writing I'm on Day 398, have saved $4,841.11 and re-gained 3,189 productive hours that would have otherwise been spent drinking or slogging through the next morning, hungover.

Each day has been easier than the last. Very rarely does the idea of having a drink even cross my mind anymore. When it does, I "play the tape forward" – visualizing how that would likely turn out -- and the thought vaporizes immediately. I continue to listen to recovery podcasts, use Abstar, read books, blogs and the MM forum, belong to the MM Absers Yahoo group, and recently joined the Women for Sobriety online community, because I don't want to get complacent in my sobriety. So, while I'm still thinking about alcohol daily, now it's in a healthy rather than obsessive manner.

I never wanted to quit for good although for many years I'd known that would be the intelligent choice. I simply didn't want to *have to stop drinking*. Now after 13 months that idea has flipped to "I don't *have to drink*." I'm loving the sound sleep, waking up refreshed and alert, I feel more consistent in mood, and have a positive outlook for the future. I can't believe I waited so long to tackle this problem, but I don't feel badly about all those years of drinking and wrestling with moderation, though. They are what brought me right here, telling you this story.

Choosing to live alcohol free was the best decision I could have made, and I feel genuinely happy and content for the first time in 25 years. There's a wonderful sense of freedom and of hope that I couldn't have imagined when I first signed up for Moderation Management.

Karin's Story: The Quiet Persistent Voice

For a long time, I had doubts and fears about my relationship with alcohol. I started drinking with friends at 14. My parents separated at 18 which I took hard. By 20 I was buying a bottle of wine on my way home from work, often finishing it. By my mid-20s, I embodied 'work hard and play hard'. Alcohol was everywhere, and the norm. All day drinking sessions meant all day hangovers, but it seemed like everyone was doing it.

However, it was about this time, in my mid-twenties, that a quiet but persistent voice in my head kept saying 'this isn't quite right, you have an unquenchable thirst for wine, you can't stop at will." It was also around that time a few of my friends were brave enough to voice their concerns for me. I was a little shaken that they had echoed these thoughts but addressing these concerns head on just felt too big. AA was mentioned but I couldn't bring myself to even consider that as an option, I wasn't at rock bottom, I didn't want to stop.

So, instead, I gave up wine for 3 months and drank beer instead, reasoning that beer wasn't as strong as wine, and I'd be giving my liver "a break." During that period, I slowly amended the rules to include anything with bubbles in, just not wine... but eventually wine worked its way back into my (almost) daily life.

A devastating bereavement followed in my late 20s and I forgot about these concerns and leaned hard into wine for support. I'd have fleeting thoughts of "I ought to really address this drinking thing" but I was keeping busy avoiding the grief, busy at work, and in life and wine was an excellent numbing and distraction tool. I excelled at work, despite the drinking, I was highly functioning and alcohol-dependent. This continued, with the quiet voice getting ever so slightly louder and louder. It was on the horizon, having to tackle this, but it just felt too insurmountable.

In my mid 30's, the hangovers started becoming crippling, the anxiety increased and the alcohol started to feel like an ever closing noose around my neck. It wasn't making me feel better anymore. I wasn't getting the high and all the grief and trauma I'd been trying to avoid would just come out in tears when I was drunk. I had a big open wound that booze helped to keep open.

After another particularly bad hangover, and another morning of completing the 'am I an alcoholic' questionnaires online, I stumbled upon moderation management, and it threw me the lifeline I needed. Giving moderation a chance, with a tested plan to follow, and a group of people to support each other was my ticket back to a healthier place. The relief I felt reading the testimonials online was overwhelming. Even more so was the relief I felt when I joined the group and found hundreds of people in my position, with all the same worries and concerns. Even better again was that there were people in the group who had overcome their drinking issues and had learned to drink moderately again. I could do this!!

I threw myself into the world of stickies, trikes and F'abs... trying to build up my small wins of a few days off in a row each week. What struck me instantly was how difficult it was to maintain this... this was a real awakening for me, in terms of how ingrained the alcohol was in my life, but I was determined to succeed. A few months in, I decided to attempt my first 30. I had only once before managed a 10-day stint, in the last 20 years. A whole month felt like a mountain to climb, but I had something to prove to myself and was excited about what it would mean if I could achieve it. With the support of the group, and publicly declaring it to a whole bunch of people, I was committed. The first two weeks were the hardest, after that the finish line was in sight. I began to reap the benefits people talked of, better sleep, less anxiety, losing weight, but most of all I felt free.

Despite this success, ironically this one month had sown a seed in my head. I knew even back then that the probable outcome for me, was that eventually I'd give up drinking for good. I think I already knew that going back to moderation was going to be hard. But now I'd seen that sobriety wasn't all bad.

However, I wasn't ready at that stage to give up, I ploughed on with my attempts to moderate. A year later I did another 30 and continued to build up 3/4 days abstinence most weeks. But on the days, I drank, I still struggled with stopping after one or two and regularly went over the recommended amount. Still, I was getting regular abs days under my belt, so it still felt like a win.

In 2017 I was diagnosed with a chronic illness, which naturally helped me pull back a little from the drinking. I drifted away from MM, but managed another 6 months' worth of breaks from drinking over one year. I was beginning to think I'd cracked it.

Last summer, despite many long periods of abstinence and much reduced levels of drinking, I had two serious binges which left me incapacitated for days. It was at this point that I knew in my heart, and my head that my drinking days were done. Despite all the effort I'd put into managing my drinking, and the partial success I'd had with that, and managing a chronic illness to boot, there were still occasions when I simple couldn't control my intake and I was done.

Done trying, done fighting, done with the effort. I signed back up to MM but this time to the mmabsers (abstainers) group. This particular group was game-changing for me. The wealth of knowledge, compassion and support was invaluable, and my abstinence journey began.

I'm now 9 months abstinent. The journey continues and life still has its bumps in the road. I still mourn for the "old me," I feel frustrated I cannot drink "like other people," but I've experienced more contentment and inner calm-happiness in the last year than in the last 25. I regularly feel relieved that I no longer fight that battle.

My journey with MM and my moderation attempts were absolutely crucial to getting me to a place where I was ready to accept that, for me, abstinence was the best option. Had I not spent those years trying, learning and slowly building up those periods of abstinent, I'd still be drinking. No question. I will be eternally grateful that MM offered me a route that I felt comfortable with to explore my issues with alcohol, with no judgement, no shame and no labels. It was my lifeline and unquestionably my lifesaver, and I made some pretty awesome friends along the way.

<u>Ginette's Story</u>: The Gift That Keeps On Giving

Sobriety surprises me with new gifts around every corner, it seems. There are the big gifts, obviously, like all the money I'm saving (Wow. Just wow. I'd be wealthy if I'd stopped drinking even a few years ago!). Then, there are the suddenly realized small gifts, like being able to look myself in the mirror without feeling disgust or shame. I didn't even realize that I had been doing that for years until I realized I WASN'T doing it. I was washing my hands in the restroom at work and looked at myself in the mirror - and I LIKED what I saw. I could LOOK at myself. Before sobriety, and even in the early days, I would glance quickly and then look away, every single time. I didn't like what I saw. It's not just personal appearance, although that of course plays into it - we never look our best hungover and rattled - it's my aura. Instead of dark and furtive and blurry, I'm clear and bright and energetic. It's in my entire physical presence, not just in my face, that my sobriety is making itself known. I'm more upright. I walk with a bounce in my step. My lips are curved upward in repose rather than scowling—I had the biggest RBF (Resting Bitch Face) in town.

It really was quite a shock to realize that I've been avoiding looking at myself for years while drinking, and another very welcome shock to see myself and be pleased at what I saw.

I was leafing through my journals of the past years and was surprised at how long I tried to moderate, how many sober days I racked up before making the final decision. It wasn't an abrupt switch. It was at least two years in the making, after having years of vague worrying about the amount I was drinking, evolving into having really bad hangovers, blackouts, feeling fuzzy for half or a whole day after drinking, and a faceplant that broke my nose (I'd forgotten about that until I ran across that journal entry.) I had a mental obsession with alcohol (did I have enough wine? Was there enough for tomorrow? Don't forget to stop and get wine!). I never remembered going to sleep when I woke up the next morning, never remembered how I got to bed. Within the last year before I went alcohol free, I had an episode where I drunkenly fell getting into bed and knocked my cheek and temple against my nightstand, creating a nice bruise. My dentist, of all people, noticed it and asked did I have to go the ER.

I was on MM for those years, trying to moderate and discovering that I could not. I tried Abstar, I tried triking and f'abs and just couldn't. The "What the Hell" attitude was strong in me and once that first drink hit my bloodstream, moderation was OUT the window. I put a couple of 30 day stretches in, realized how much better I felt NOT drinking, and decided to go full abs on May 1, 2018. I didn't want to go to AA. I just didn't feel like it would help me. I had found people that I identified with on the MM main list, and thought I'd try the mmabsers group and found an amazing, supportive community of people who were just like me, including some friends from the main list who had crossed over. We share our struggles and our successes, our milestones and our fears, and are stronger together. Knowing that I'm not alone in this journey, having the group to vent or share with, has made a tremendous difference to me.

I am LIVING instead of dying by inches, drowning in the wine bottle. And, among all the other gifts that sobriety has given me, I am amazingly bruise free, for the first time in many years, and if I get a bruise, I can tell you exactly where and when I got it!

Electra Lou's Story:
Perm Abs As A Choice, Not As A Last Resort

I don't remember how I found Moderation Management – probably by desperately googling "do I drink too much", or "how can I control my drinking". What I do remember is finding a welcoming community of people who were all struggling like I was and who were eager to share tips, tricks and stories. For close to two years, I posted on the discussion lists and tracked my drinks. I shared my small successes (only three drinks at happy hour this past Wednesday!) and discouraging setbacks (another blackout this weekend and my boyfriend is super angry at me again). No one ever judged me or told me that I was a hopeless alcoholic. At that point in time, MM was exactly what I needed: a place to explore my relationship to drinking and experiment with changes and tweaks to my behavior.

In many ways, the wider MM community was my first introduction to people who were toying with the idea of sobriety. I knew that AA and its ilk existed – but I was resolutely set against going down that path, for a variety of reasons. Slowly, however, I began to hear people whispering on the main lists about a sub-group of MM: people who had gone "perm abs", or permanently abstinent, and who for all intents and purposes did not drink anymore. Perm abs seemed like a different beast than the sobriety conferred by the label "alcoholic": it seemed like a choice, one that was freely made and could, potentially though rarely, be renegotiated at a later date.

I joined the MM list for "absers", or people who had decided long-term abstinence was for them, the day after my best friend presented me with an ultimatum: drink and lose his friendship, or sober up and remain in his life. While I was initially resigned to a life without fun and joy,

I suppose I was finally also ready to contemplate a life without alcohol.

It has been almost four years now, and I have not had another drink. My little corner of MM has been an invaluable tool for my sobriety. We are the people who were drawn by the alternative approach to alcohol that MM provided, but who ultimately decided that true freedom was complete abstinence from alcohol. What is unique in this approach is that I do not feel defined by a label (I am no more an alcoholic than anyone else who consumes an addictive substance and becomes dependent on it, be it chocolate, cigarettes, alcohol or heroin) and I do not feel trapped by a rigid set of diktats. It is my choice not to drink: because drinking does not do good things to my mind, body or heart; because drinking takes me out of the present moment and steals time away from the real business of living; because I do not need an addictive substance to feel joy, sadness, excitement, love or despair. In fact, I can now access the whole range of human emotions and experiences in ways that I had never imagined. I am not powerless: I am incredibly powerful, as I have overcome a physical, psychological and social addiction to a substance that is simultaneously glorified and demonized by most of society. Most importantly, I am free: free of the endless chattering brain that told me I needed a drink, wanted a drink, deserved a drink. Life, it turns out, is infinitely bigger and brighter than the bottom of a bottle.

Mike's Story:

I was active in AA (Alcoholics Anonymous) and sober for almost eleven years when I started to become disenchanted. I was thinking about returning to drinking and wondering if I really was an 'alcoholic' after all, or if I had just bought into that belief all those years.

When I started drinking again, I joined MM. I worked on moderation for seven years before deciding to go permanently abstinent. During the seven years working towards moderation, I found it difficult and often failed severely at it. I recognized that I have a mental obsession with alcohol and the only way for me to find peace of mind was through being completely alcohol free, yet again. I found being sober and part of the MM Abstinence community much less restrictive and open-minded than my previous experience at AA.

I remain very active in MM and have dedicated myself to those MM members who choose abstinence as the Coordinator of the mmabsers community for over nine years now. In the beginning of my abstinence, I also attended AA and SMART Recovery regularly.

The MM Abstinence community is a tolerant, non-judgmental environment where each individual decides for themselves the path they wish to pursue. If folks are inclined to sobriety, I and the other members of mmabsers are very happy to help them along the way by offering support and sharing our experiences of the life we have found to be more rewarding and enriching without the influence of alcohol. I have had the joy of seeing so many folks get and stay sober and find much more peace, gratitude and balance in their lives. For this I am humbly grateful.

Below is a more detailed account of "my story" in answer to an email from one of my fellow mmabsers. It's long with lots of ups and downs and back and forths, like life.

Mike,

I think you said in one of your recent posts that you stopped drinking for 10 years (?) and then went back to it, only to make the final decision to quit all together. Assume the latter came when things went off the rails again.

Curious, what led you to resume after such a long abstinence stretch?

Was it successful initially (e.g., moderation) and how did that phase progress before it went off the rails?

As I've mentioned, no real intention to resume drinking, although part of me is having the "was I really that bad" thought thread passing across the radar. Most recent version was give it a year off and then re-evaluate.

Would appreciate hearing about your experience.

Greg

OK, Greg. Here goes. Feel like I'm answering questions for a college paper. No wonder I never graduated. Could've also had something to do with all the drugs and alcohol. I always feel pressured when asked to write something rather than just letting things flow from myself and my ownstream of consciousness, with spontaneous inspiration. But I will do my best.

I'm not a big fan of the term "my story" coined at AA meetings.

Because one's life's story and their alcohol abuse are not one and the
same nor could they ever be told in an hour-long talk nor in an email.
But here goes.

Mike

The answer to your first questions is, yes. I was sober for 10 1/2 years. From 11/28/91 to 4/27/2002. I joined AA for those sober years. And, yes, I did decide to go back to being sober when things went off the rails again, but it was definitely not that black and white. So, I will try to answer the questions: **why I got sober in the first place?** (my question), **what led me to resume after such a long abstinence stretch?** (your question and an important one), **was it 'successful' initially (e.g. moderation)?** and **how did that phase progress before it went off the rails?**

I will also throw in, hopefully, some serious thoughts or contemplation on the insidious thought that we all have had and that you have expressed here for yourself "**was I really that bad?**"

So, I was born in a log cabin in 1856 where we consumed massive amounts of cocaine at birth. Oops! Wrong story. That's my Narcotics Anonymous story.

OK, I am from Brooklyn, NY. Son of a NYC taxi driver and housewife. At the ripe young age of 11, I began experimenting with pot, drugs and alcohol. It was pretty darn illicit then. This is pre-Beatles craze and hippies, etc. But that was to come straight away. I was pretty insecure and somewhat isolated yet I had sort of a regular growing up with playing lots of sports and friends and doing school. In Junior High, I had two friends who'd cut class with me and smoke and drink and, yes, sniff glue. I also experimented with heroin with my brother. We thought it was cocaine the first time, but it was dope. This was around age 13. In high school, I did as well as I did in Junior High. I had friends who did drugs and alcohol, but in high school I became friends with a whole group of guys who liked to indulge mostly in weed and drinking and some acid. Through high school and my wasted ungraduated college years, I did every drug known to mankind at the time, especially a lot of acid and heroin, quaaludes, ups and downs, and Dewars White Label and Heineken or Colt45 Malt Liquor, Ballentine Ale (by the quart). Booze was always in the mix, especially with pot, acid or uppers.

I started playing drums at 13. We jammed in the local park and at people's homes a lot. And, we all hung out at a local bar where everyone knew us.

Dewars on the rocks-n-Heineken again. It was fun. Fun and crazy years. My gal broke up with me at 20 years old and I had my first real depression, and I started hitting the heroin harder and sort of got me a bad habit for about two years. Just before my 23rd birthday on April 2, 1977, I went into a drug treatment program named Daytop Village. This is a 24-hour therapeutic community (TC) where I lived in upstate NY for 13 months and then in a re-entry facility in Manhattan for another 11 months or so until I got my apartment in Brooklyn. I had girlfriend, she moved in with me, and I was "sober." I felt like a man. As part of graduation from the drug program they gave you your "drinking privileges". You went to a bar with a mentor type guy (my girlfriend came too) and had some drinks and was warned to be careful. "Since you were addicted to drugs," they told me, "it's possible you could become the same with alcohol." But the thinking in those days was that most graduates and staff members could drink. Bullshit!

This is where my "story" changes quite a bit. This was late 1979. I was in this bar in Queens and I remember those two long neck 6 oz bottles of Pabst Blue Ribbon. I was glowing. I had a smile from ear to ear and I drove off into the sunset to my apartment in Brooklyn with my beloved girlfriend.

I got a job in Manhattan and commuted. My gal and I drank wine (she loved wine). I didn't but it got me high and gave me heartburn. Our relationship ended, sadly, and I had two friends who also graduated from Daytop with me living in my neighborhood. They both enjoyed their liquor. One was a gin drinker, the other vodka. I drank both but took vodka to be my number one. Although now I was drinking every kind of hard liquor there was, even tequila at times, a flash back to those jams in the park with my friends – friends I no longer associated with because I did not do drugs anymore and I was "sober".

Well, in 1980 I began to know what blackouts are. Had my first in a bar on 34th street in Manhattan. Left the bar to catch the train on a Friday night to go home to Brooklyn only to awaken on a subway train in Harlem around 11:30 am. At least the train was headed south towards Brooklyn. Folks had beach chairs and stuff. It was summer. As I mentioned, I was working in Manhattan at the time, living in Brooklyn and made one particular bar/restaurant my home. I loved it there. It was very colorful. I knew the owner and his family and everyone who came there, even some celebrities. Was a grand party.

I told my brother one day when we took a pot break outside the bar that it had happened, that my addiction to alcohol was as great if not greater than my addiction to heroin was.

That was really when I came to know I had crossed the line and was perhaps "alcoholic". I wouldn't take drugs. That I knew was a problem but alcohol, sure. And, I was around drugs in the bar all the time, late nights, taxis, after-hour joints. I was to learn the expression from AA meetings that since I stopped using drugs and only drank that I had "switched seats on the Titanic."

In 1982, I got very ill and was diagnosed with having Hep C (they didn't call it that then, but that's what it was – I did get treated for it finally in 1998). But what I did have was active Epstein-Barr Virus (probably resulting from a very bad episode of Herpes back in my Manhattan Daytop year '79) and this led to Chronic Fatigue which I still deal with today. Today they call it CFS/ME and I will leave that alone for now. Anyway, I was out on disability for 5 months and doctors told me not to drink. So, I just stayed home and vegged out. My girlfriend and mother brought me food, etc. Doctors then felt that the chronic persistent hepatitis (that's what they called Hep C back then) was my more serious problem, so I was told to limit my drinking to white wine or beer and to be moderate. So that meant to me, back to the bar and back to buying liters and half gallons of vodka for the house and of course plenty of good German beer. I drank my heaviest from '83 until Nov 91 when I finally went into AA. Didn't care about the "liver disease." I also got married for a couple years (or should I say I took a hostage).

I started dating my current wife in early '90. It was a party at first until she started to see that the Dudley Moore cavalier drunk ended up pissing hotel beds, passed out against her Manhattan apartment building and worse. She started putting the clamps to me and I started to resent it and feel like I was in a trap. The trap of really admitting and accepting I was an alcoholic now. How'd that happen? Jeez. Fuck that, can't be.

Reluctantly, I attended an AA meeting and hated it and didn't go back. I had to attend my first AA meeting in 1978 as part of my graduation from Daytop to warn me what could happen if I drank. I remember that one. It was in the village in NYC and near the Bowery, so it was, well different. Lots of skid row people... and me :-)

Then on the eve of Thanksgiving 1991, I started at my bar in the afternoon. WTF, it's a long holiday weekend. By the time evening rolled around I was to pick up my girlfriend (wife to be) uptown from where I worked (on 23rd street), at 43rd on the east side and drive up to Westchester with her and her 4-year-old daughter for Thanksgiving at her sister's house. She caught on that I was wasted and told me to leave. It was her car I was driving. So, I left. Took a cab back down to my bar. A blackout ensued. A bad one. Don't know how I got home to my condo in Queens at the time. I mean I do have some grey memories of being sort of comatose in a cab company and not being able to get words out. I awoke in my bed somehow, bruised badly, my face smashed in, my new sneakers gone, black socks, wrenched back. Neighbors told me that cops had to come to help me into my apartment as I fell down a flight of marble stairs and landed with my face into a cinder block wall. I have more "battle scars" from other such incidents. And please

I am not trying to tell a "war story" here" folks. I'm just telling it.

I got in a shower that morning and, tail between my legs, drove to where my wife-to-be was. That was Nov 28, 1991 and I was to get sober for 10 1/2 years behind all that. I found an AA meeting finally, after hating all of them, in Manhattan at lunch time and went to it daily. It was different, sort of cool, regular people, most with jobs, commuters, and some locals, and it was not as religious as a lot of the others seemed to me. Over time, I started to like the meeting a lot and the people there and I did start to feel some kind of "spiritual thing" too. But it was also very secular and real. Folks there knew the neighborhood (my drinking neighborhood), the bars, the lingo, the NYC eclectic kind of feel. So, it helped me to acquire a year and more...

In '92 my job relocated me from the Manhattan office to Long Island. The company helped me financially to move and purchase a home. That was great. We got married and pregnant and had my son in '93 while my stepdaughter turned 7. I joined AA on Long Island and life was good. I was pretty active in AA back then and stayed so until something changed....

Now finally, I get to some of the answers.

April 27, 2002. On that day I attended a sweet 16 for our neighbor's daughter. My daughter was also 16 at the time. They were very close. The girls and their friends were coming of age. The street I lived on was a cul de sac and lots of families and kids moved in after us. We were a tight block. I became an avid runner. There were block parties and bonfires over the years and lots of heavy drinkers on my block, including Halloween expeditions where parents took along a little helper (that one's for you Marco).

Over the years, I often felt like the outsider, the leper, with the stick up my ass. I avoided a lot of get togethers because of the drinking. And, I started to want to partake but sort of buried it. Then, I started to feel emboldened and had thoughts like, I'm so disciplined in all areas of life, exercise, diet, work, who's to say I cannot discipline alcohol? Maybe I really wasn't an alcoholic but bought into it at AA all those years? Maybe I was only addicted to it for a few years (ha ha) and I'm in a "different station" in life now, more mature, raised kids, not a single, cavalier asshole anymore.

I started to resent the AA meetings after all those years of buying in. I started to feel like I just wanted out of the kool-aid. I stopped going, gave up my "commitment" there (as I was very active). In my mind I knew I wanted to try drinking again. It began as that little pinhole in my brain that said maybe I wasn't that bad, maybe I am mature enough now to control it like "others".

So, at that sweet sixteen party, I was sitting at my table, I was watching my wife, daughter and all the sweet sixteeners dancing. I said to myself, boy, it would be nice to finally dance with a drink under my belt. So, I got up and went to the bar which fortunately was around the back from the dining and dancing area. Quickly ordered a vodka on the rocks and drank it down fast, returned to my seat. I felt nothing. Bummer. And the drink tasted real (not watered down). So, I went for another and did the same and returned to my seat. Barely the slightest buzz. Jeez I thought I would have no tolerance. Not true.

I went to dance and enjoyed it with that slight buzz and I was happy. After we returned to our seats, I was restless in that I really wanted more than the slightest hint of a buzz. After all, Jeez. All these years and I barely feel it.

Someone left over almost a full glass of white wine so with the greatest of class, I grabbed it and gulped it down when no one was looking. After a bit, I felt the buzz was reasonable enough and I had snuck enough and returned to dancing, and I enjoyed myself. I drove my family home and never said a word and I felt nothing but good.

At this stage in my life, my focus was on so much else other than drinking. I maintained my running routine, work and diet and family responsibilities and just stopped doing AA. I was involved in a civic action with others in my community so that kept me busy. I felt free. No more AA and I could drink and not run out and buy a bottle of booze. In fact, I was not to drink again for 3 months. I didn't even think much about it. Only that I had done it and never told anyone, especially my wife.

Three months later we were at another party – an affair, fundraiser for the civic action I was involved with. I usually drank cranberry juice and club soda at this kind of event so when I had the same only with vodka my wife was not suspicious. I had two and the experience was exactly like how it went down at the sweet sixteen. No problem. Felt great. Didn't run out for more.

I thought I had arrived. A few weeks later I told my wife about all I had done.

She freaked. Very angry and scared. But I had started reading Stanton Peele and all the harm reduction activists and started to believe. I was "possessed" and started to sell her or should I say sell myself and my bullshit. This went on for a long time. Finally, she gave in and we went to a tennis event and I had a couple of mixed vodka drinks. Inside she knew better but would have loved it if I could drink like her.

One day at a party I got drunk and she said, "That's it". "But I drank too much too fast," I said, "so I'll just need to learn."

I looked into MM after yet another bad drinking experience. Again, I sold myself to her and started against her approval with MM. Off and on for 7 years I got very active with MM. I did all I could to prove that I could abstar my way to success. It was always work although at times I thought I did well enough. Every time I did a little too much I would pull in the reins and try to tweak my program. I was on the Listserv for a couple years but I got more involved with MM in NYC live.

Bottom line is, when I first went back to drinking it was not what I expected.

In AA they say "the disease is doing push-ups in the parking lot." In other words, "the progressive disease of alcoholism will be as strong as when you last stopped if not stronger." So, folks like me feared they'd drink and couldn't stop. But I did. I thought all that was bullshit now and that I had arrived to the land of no more alcoholism-free at last. Jeez, a few drinks and not even a desire for 3 months and then just a few drinks. Back to life, running schedule, etc. Man I got it all under control. Maybe I wasn't an alcoholic after all, maybe I wasn't that bad, maybe it was just a period of my life and now things are different.

NOT!!!

Shit got raggedy real fast. Within months after that 3-month stretch, I started to know that I was trying to prove something, that I was "possessed" by it and MM was my way to make it all acceptable to me, my wife and kids. Some bought my bullshit. I mean, people who are not problem drinkers don't get it, and people that are, are glad to have you on board.

There was one bad blackout and Mrs. mike called me on it. It was horrible for me. I could not escape that reality and in 2007, I reluctantly went 15 months "sober" and joined MMabsers. But, I still had reservations and I told the group I was returning to drink and left. For four months I drank but really tried to control it again. I started drinking half pints of vodka. It was not enough but I did it. On July 18th, I drove to upstate NY to see a concert with my brother and a friend. Since I was driving, I did not drink going there. I drank a half pint at the show and drove home.

The next morning on the 19th, I was watching the British Open golf and went out to my garage to my golf bag where there was a big bottle of vodka and started in. This was close to noon time. A little later my wife asked if I'd like to join her and my son to go see the new Harry Potter movie. I was happy to be asked as we were living together but separated at that time. I drove about 5 miles towards the movie when they realized I was drunk. My wife took over the wheel and drove me back home.

I do not remember any of this as I was in a blackout. I only remember a few little things. I don't remember leaving the house, getting in the car, anything, but I remember my son, who was 16 at the time, in the back seat. He was crying and he yelled "stop it already." I guess we were arguing but those words mean a lot to me today as I just started to tear up here and now.

I awoke the next afternoon in the basement of my house which is where I lived then. The vodka bottle from my garage was at the head of my bed close to empty. My right hand was swollen. Think I found the knuckle imprint upstairs in some sheet rock. I vaguely remember trying to put a record on stereo turntable and playing my drum set and smoking a cigar.

That's all I remember when I awoke. It was July 20, 2009. I was so full of remorse, shame, guilt and such great sadness came over me. I felt that I had done the unthinkable. I could have killed my wife and son. And just imagine if I did and I had survived. Then I realized, that this could happen again. I drove drunk for years in the 70's and especially 80's and early 90's.

I had driven my son and his friends a few times to events with a good buzz and I remember my son looking over at me, knowingly. I remember getting drunk when my daughter needed help with a science project and on a Father's Day. My kids knew me sober for 10 1/2 years and during my 7 years trying to moderate they saw me be obnoxious and several other things. One day my son said to me, "the father I know just isn't there when you drink."

So, after that blackout I was devastated. I went to a friend who I knew for many years who was attending a SMART Recovery group nearby and who, like me, had been a long-time member of AA on Long Island. We knew there was good in AA but also a lot of crap too. So, I returned to my SMART friends and I also started attending an AA meeting in a different area than my old home group. It was a convenient lunch time meeting. I stayed off and on for 3 years and am still good friends with the SMART friends only I'm not living there anymore.

Of course, I got back involved with MMabsers immediately too. This is my one home that I've stayed in for the past 9 years of continued sobriety and beforehand as well. And I'm looking forward to returning to Long Island where my daughter recently bought a house and moved in with her boyfriend. Then I'll see some of my old SMART Recovery friends, although our meeting has disbanded. My daughter is now 32 and my son is now 25 and he just bought a house in Philadelphia with his girlfriend. We're going up for Thanksgiving. My wife's

65th the day after. For many years Thanksgiving Day was my sober anniversary although the date Nov 28th was the actual one in 1991. But, man-o-man, I am so grateful.

So, I try to remain humble and find truth in my bullshit. And the work always continues for me. I think service to others is most important in life and helps the giver immensely.

Thank you All.

CHAPTER 6: RETURN TO MODERATION

"She would be a new person, she vowed. They said no matter how far a mule travels it can never come back a horse, but she would show them all." — Junot Díaz, <u>The Brief Wondrous Life of Oscar Wao</u>

Forever is a transformative vow. When we make a forever promise, we become a person who holds to a change in our life as permanent, a change that we will not forsake, no matter what other life changes our future holds. Those who make a forever vow believe that upholding that vow will serve them in the best way possible for the rest of their lives. For them, the vow to quit drinking forever means freedom and empowerment to direct their full-attention and time to other areas of their life—to never again be distracted or dominated by alcohol.

But, for others, a forever vow seems another form of enslavement, a loss of freedom and an admission of powerlessness. When a person is considering abstinence, forever can be a deal breaker because it is still too foreign a concept to make a forever promise to uphold.

When a person has experienced a long period of successful abstinence and has done the work and self-exploration to build a new life and new self, they often discover they are not the same person who let alcohol claim control before.

Many problem drinkers started drinking in their teens and never fully developed other coping methods or a full collection of interests that didn't include alcohol. Alcohol held them back from developing their full selves. However, through long periods of abstinence—several years for many—some have filled those deficiencies with substance, valuable parts and pieces and essences of themselves that were missing. They know how hard they worked and the pain they had to endure to get to where they are. Because of their prolonged abstinence, they do not feel as susceptible to alcohol's power as they once were. They are no longer the same person.

For others, moderation was their norm for most of their adult life until tragedy or upheaval caused them to stray into harmful drinking routines to cope. Once life returned to normal, or as normal as it could, they found themselves caught in the web of their habit and abstinence was the quickest, most dependable way out. Through abstinence, they were able to find their way back to themselves, their once moderate selves. They begin resent that a temporary aberration in their drinking signifies to others that they have to quit drinking forever.

Why? Why would they want to introduce a substance that had caused them so much pain and heartache back into their life?

The answer is different for each person, but the distinction has to be made that they are not willing to let the pain and heartache back in, that they want the same things that moderate drinkers want from drinking. Ceremony. Celebration. Connection. But this time around, they also want Control.

Can't they have those things without alcohol? Of course, and they, unlike others who have not been abstinent for a long period, have the nuanced skills to get through any situation without alcohol. They know it can be done, because they've done it.

It comes back to that word "enjoyable" as in "a small but enjoyable part of our life." Those who choose to return to drinking after a problematic relationship with alcohol followed by a long period of abstinence, desire alcohol as a special indulgence, something out of the ordinary-an exclamation point at the end of a well-executed sentence. They are not searching for something lacking in their lives. Unlike most of our society who have never lived the abstinent lifestyle, they no longer have a grasping need to fill their empty spaces with alcohol, they know that alcohol, too much or too often, only leaves bigger holes.

They have gained the knowledge that alcohol will never measure up to an extraordinary life. In a world in which regular drinking has become ordinary, they've lived extraordinary.

STORIES:

Chris's Story:

I started MM in 2014 after being in AA for 5 ½ years. I have been successfully moderating my drinking since.

I grew up in an environment where drinking was everywhere. It was what you did at celebrations, birthdays, funerals, and just about anything else. It was also a coping tool, so when things were not going well, alcohol was the answer. It is, after all, known for this, giving immediate pleasure and reducing pain.

I know this, but most of my life has been mindlessly going through this as a habit, the norm, just what I am used to because it is comfortable. What isn't comfortable is saying 'no' when someone asks me to have a drink with them.

In 2009, I was drinking to excess. I was in a horrible situation with work and hiding my drinking from my husband. Sometimes I was even drinking 1 – 2 bottles of wine a night and not making it up to the bedroom because I was so drunk. Something came to me that I needed help. So, I went to an AA meeting, which was a breath of fresh air to me and just what I needed at the time. I enjoyed the community and support and did not mind the higher power references. It is just what it is.

Although I was embedded in the AA culture, I knew that there must be another way and did not buy into the idea that 'to drink is to die' or 'half measures avail us nothing'. I am not different. I just know we have more information now about being mindful. I know I am not a normie (read paragraphs above; drinking is important socially and family-wise for me). But again, I believe we know more today, and I am a curious person, so I wanted to see if there was some research on *moderate* drinking.

Like others, I googled *Moderate Drinking*, and Moderation Management appeared in my search. I sought support and discussed what others thought about moderate drinking and whether it is possible.

I have been successfully moderating for 4 years and continue to learn about my motivations, triggers, and how to live a balanced life. It is not sheer willpower but being mindful. The same consciousness that comes from deciding to be a good person, try to work hard, work out, learn an instrument. All of these are ways that I continue to grow and be a better person.

These terms are not new, but I know that if I am growing and learning, I'll be okay and will be the person I aspire to be. I have a Life Coach and attend an online MM meeting weekly. These keep me accountable and ensure that if I do slip up (which happens less and less), I have a safe place to share and be compassionate with myself. I am in this for the long haul, to be balanced, face life's challenges and enjoy an adult beverage every so often as a 'small, but enjoyable part of my life.'

So, for me, my success comes in continually learning about my motivations, what I can do to follow the definition of a Moderate Drinker (have hobbies, have non-drinking friends, have other things to do to relax) and basically, I have tools that I use to feel confident and not mindless.

Most importantly, like anything that I think is important, I try to stay engaged at whatever level I can: attend meetings, read the Moderation.org website, talk to a Life Coach or therapist. It is working for me, and I hope for you all reading this as well.

Nora D.'s Story: Cause or Solution

"...Alcohol! The cause of... and solution to... all of life's problems."
—Homer Simpson

For fans of "The Simpsons" television show, this line is classic Homer – a good dollop of wisdom coupled with a complete lack of interest in changing. Both sad and funny.

Aaah, the eternal paradox of alcohol. Alcohol has caused so many problems in my life, and yet, when I'm feeling bored, anxious, sad, lonely, overwhelmed, happy, celebratory, excited – in other words, feeling anything – it seems a reasonable and even perfect solution.

I drank eagerly for 12 years, from age 14 to 26. Then I stopped drinking for 23 years and 3 months (not that I was counting). Eight years ago, I started drinking again and saw that I was still eager for that drink. Eager for the buzz, the camaraderie with other drinkers, the easing of tension, the release of whatever negative feelings I was having.

But the problem with drinking is that it's a temporary fix for my permanent problem – the inability to sit with feelings, whether good or bad. I always want to eliminate the bad and enhance the good. If I'm sad, I want to be less sad; if I'm happy, I want to be more happy. And alcohol does fix that – for a little while.

But in attempting to fix a single problem, alcohol has caused more problems. Like blackouts where I remember nothing. How did I get home? What did I say on the phone? How did I embarrass myself? Who can I call who will tell me what I said or did and not judge me? Or brownouts, where I kind of sort of remember parts of the occasion, but not quite. So many hours trying to piece together missing time and agonizing over what I do remember.

I'm lucky to be alive after all the times I've driven drunk. I'm lucky to still have friends considering what a demanding and needy person I was during the days of my heaviest drinking. I've thrown up more times and in more places than I can count. I've spent mornings struggling to put on my mascara because my hands are shaking and my head is spinning. I've showed up to work drunk, either freshly so (which got me fired), or still drunk from the night before. I got pregnant and had an abortion as a consequence of a drunken one-night stand. I've wallowed in angst for days after an episode of overdrinking. These are all problems.

So why would anyone with those experiences ever pick up a drink again, especially after such a long period of abstinence? I could say, well, my new husband likes to drink, so it must be his fault. Or I've matured and it's no longer a problem like it was in my wayward youth. And those explanations are valid. I like to drink with my husband. I do have a different perspective and maturity after decades of abstinence. But when I've had a few too many and am regretful the next day and asking myself why why why, the answer is always the same: I like to drink. I just like to drink.

But if I want alcohol to be more of a solution than a cause, I have to learn to manage drinking. Or at least give it a shot (pun intended). And that has been happening – I've been slowly and steadily learning, growing, and changing. One of the most impactful strategies I've used is getting support. Just knowing that there are others who have the same challenges is such a gigantic relief. And there's such a wide array of organizations these days to let me know I'm not alone. That's been incredibly beneficial for the big picture.

For the little picture, the day-to-day goal of not over drinking, one of my best tools is having periods of abstinence. Abstinence clears my head and gives me the all-important reminder: I don't NEED to drink. I don't HAVE to drink. It's such a valuable reset, helping me to break the habit. I have so much pride in myself after a period of abstinence. I've accepted myself for who I am (someone who likes to drink and who can easily overdo) yet rejected always giving in to self-defeating sabotaging behavior. I become confident that my life and myself are just fine the way they are and all my feelings are gifts that don't need to be ignored or enhanced.

It can be tricky drinking again after a period of abstinence. The first few years after I started drinking again were littered with over-drinking episodes. But in time, with support and time spent abstaining (a day, a week, a month, whatever), I've found my tolerance for alcohol is reduced to the point where I simply can't drink as much as I used to. And my tolerance for the physical and emotional consequences of over-drinking is also reduced, to the point that I'm actually able to think ahead to those consequences and not take that first (or next) drink.

Abstinence can be a way of life or one of many management strategies for problem drinkers. The most important thing I can say about abstinence is that there is absolutely no downside to not drinking. None. It may not feel that way when life hits me hard or I'm just plain bored or feel desperate to change my feelings, but the physical and emotional benefits of abstinence are always

– and I can't emphasize "always" enough – greater than the temporary, and often dubious, benefits of drinking.

Bee's Story: Power Restored

"I will not spend the rest of my golden years with a drunk." Those were the words that my husband spoke one morning after I once again embarrassed him in front of his friends at a gathering. There was something in his voice that resonated he meant it this time – no more warnings. We had both recently retired and were living the dream, with many healthy years ahead to enjoy the fruits of planning and saving during long and intense careers. The thought of facing the future without him was terrifying.

The following day I browsed online for an abstinence program— I perused Smart Recovery, Women for Sobriety and a few others. I even looked at online AA meetings, although I had been an AA member in the past and swore I could never embrace powerlessness again. Moderation Management popped up on my screen and the rest is history for me.

Many people can state a reason or timeline for their propensity towards alcohol, but for me it was "love at first sip." I was an over-achiever in high school, insecure, a rule-follower, and didn't have a drink until I was 19 years old. When I felt the effects of my first beer, it was as though I had discovered the magic elixir for all my anxieties. Drinking became my weekend go-to.

My progression into heavy drinking took a mere five years. By the age of 24, I was drinking nearly every night, but luckily managed to earn two college degrees. When I married at age 25, my new husband liked to drink too since he had just gotten home from a war. He soon matured out of that troubled phase of his life whereas I continued my drinking ways. Within two years, my drinking had become a serious bone of contention in our marriage. I repeatedly promised to cut back but resorted to hiding and sneaking my booze stash, quite successfully, for several years.

I had a child at age 30 and my drinking toned down somewhat, although it was still a problem in my marriage. I struggled with varying degrees of success and failure for several more years, mainly using sheer willpower. By this time, I was acutely aware of my serious problem. There were no programs except Alcoholics Anonymous at that time; the internet was still young. Eventually I quit drinking entirely, joined AA, and abstained completely for six years. I attended AA meetings in church basements and community centers, always staying away from my own community, which I taught in. I attended AA for 18 months, and then spent 4.5 years abstaining on my own. The issue of powerlessness was always in the back of my mind—how can I be powerless over a substance? Was I really powerless? And if so, why could I abstain despite not attending weekly AA meetings? What happened to my power before and how did I get it back?

I can't remember any specific event which resulted in my drinking again, it happened gradually over several months. During that time, I remembered that AA taught me I would immediately pick up my "alcoholism" right where I had left off; in fact, ahead of where I had left off. Since that didn't happened to me, I thought I must not be an alcoholic! What a marvelous revelation! I wish I had known then what I know now—that our alcohol journeys are all different and we don't all fit the same mold. If I realized that, I would have been more on guard.

Somehow, I was able to moderate on my own for about a decade. I had a few immoderate experiences but did quite well with no outside support system. I had learned a great deal during my six years of abstaining—about my triggers and such. I had also become more self-confident with age. I do believe we change throughout life, oftentimes for the good. I felt that my character and wisdom had both grown tremendously over the years. What may be a problem at age 30, therefore, may not be a problem 20 years later. I have a sister who had a serious alcohol issue due to a horrific life experience. She morphed out of the heavy drinking on her own and seldom drinks anymore. I do not believe in final, lifelong diagnoses and sentences for issues such as drinking.

Eventually I became complacent and old drinking habits creeped back in during and around the time of my retirement. I was having brownouts, horrendous hangovers, and, occasional "hairs of the dog." And, of course, *sneaking a little* here and there crept back into my routine. It wasn't too many months before my husband of 30+ years made that echoing statement, "I will not spend the rest of my golden years with a drunk." Thus, the beginning of my power-seeking journey in Moderation Management.

The first MM concept that I grasped onto was "toolbox" & I quickly set out to fill my virtual box with tools that worked for me. I joined the drink-tracker, Abstar, and also designed my own personal spreadsheet; I have used this spreadsheet for the past 10 years. I also began strict spacing of my drinks and I defriended Mr. Smirnoff, my BFF.

In analyzing my drinking, I realized that I could more easily abstain in social situations and I actually preferred to have drinks in the controlled environment of home. We are each different and what works for one may not necessarily work for another. In Moderation Management we call it YMMV – your moderation may vary.

I read about and practiced the five P's of forming and maintaining a habit:

Patience+Priority+Planning+Practice+Perseverance=Power

It's been a slow, personal journey of baby steps, but I have achieved a moderation level that is acceptable to both myself and my spouse. Yes, we are living out our golden years together, as we worked and planned for. No more all-day hangovers, guilty lapses of memory, shameful behavior, or fearful feelings of powerlessness.

I'm so grateful to have my power back!

Dan's Story:

I had two major transition periods in my life. I was found guilty of a felony drug charge when I was 18 years old. I was, essentially, on probation from the time I was

13 to 22, and I had the mindset that I was bound to go in and out of prison the rest of my life or die young. Of course, lots of alcohol and drug use occurred during those times.

Then, at 25 years old, I experienced my first major transition.

I decided, at that point, that I wanted to have a life in which I would be able to support a family if I wanted to start a family. I did not want to be homeless or go to prison. My mindset had changed. I began to transition from the streets to higher education. I earned my associates' degree and was awarded the inspirational achievement award for going from a life on the streets to getting a college degree.

I left town to live in a dorm at a college, and I began working toward a Bachelor's degree. In the last year of my four-year effort to achieve my associate degree, I was introduced to the 12-step support culture and I continued to be a part of the 12-step support culture as I went on to attain my Bachelor's degree. There was a big problem though. As the years went by, my drinking got worse, and I was highly agitated by feeling trapped in the 12-step support culture. I was psychologically trapped because I had been misled to believe many of the mantras stated in the 12-step support culture. Namely, that I could never drink a drop of alcohol again, nothing else will work, and that I needed to keep working the 12 steps, working with a sponsor, sponsor others, and attend meetings for a lifetime, otherwise, I was doomed to die without them. My life was threatened if I left, but my drinking was getting to be the worse it had ever been in my life. I tried a church-based support group called Celebrate Recovery. I decided I was not compatible with that program either, but I did gain two things. First, in the preface of the Celebrate Recovery bible, I read Rick Warren's concern about the theology of the 12-step program. It was the first time in four years that I heard any criticism of Alcoholics Anonymous (AA). Second, I began working through the Celebrate Recovery workbooks, and it felt good to answer open-ended questions about myself rather than have everything dictated to me as immutable facts in the 12-step culture. I came to a question in the workbook that asked if there was anything in my life that I was doing over and over again and expecting different results. I was thinking "hell yea," I keep going to these 12-step meetings. Enough was enough, I was not going to continue doing the same thing over and over again, the 12-step program, and expect different results. I began seeking other answers.

I first began seeking other answers by majoring in psychology, and I found my first answer in a course about group theory. Dr. Stanton Peele was quoted in the textbook, and I immediately identified with what he was talking about. He was talking about the psychological phenomena of a type of brainwashing occurring in the 12-step support culture. My healing had begun. Someone understood me, and they were legitimate with expert authority on addictions. I also had a counselor and a detox worker say to me they didn't think AA was "all that." At the time, I thought these statements sounded blasphemous, but they were right. I finally made a break for it from the 12-step support culture.

I found support at leavingaa.com and I became a "Friend of Monica's." Monica Richardson was an AA member for 36 years when she left. She has a blogtalk radio podcast, and it was through her platform that I discovered Moderation Management (MM).

I dived right into MM. I was so very happy and relieved to hear people make more sense to me about alcohol issues. I bought almost every book the MM website had listed, and it was from these books that I discovered a whole world of progressive addiction treatment leaders, researchers, and writers. I began attending face-to-face meetings, online meetings, and recording my drinks on the Abstar tool. I even went to visit one of the authors of the Responsible Drinking book, Dr. Marc Kern, and asked him to sign my book and take a picture. I bought MM merchandise like shirts and a teddy bear. Someone on the online chat said the power of MM comes from the MM community, this community helped save me when nothing else would. For the first time since being told in the 12-step support culture that I was powerless over alcohol, I moderated a fifth of whiskey under the MM guidelines. I was shocked and elated. I went on to rigidly moderate my whiskey use for four years! I was also privileged to have my story published under a pseudonym in Dr. Lance Dode's book *"The Sober Truth: Debunking the Bad Science Behind 12 Step Programs and the Rehab Industry."*

Because I assumed I had a serious substance use issue in the past, it was highly important to moderate exactly as MM outlined. I almost had a nervous breakdown when I first drank more than four drinks in one sitting, but I went on to discover my personal strengths, knowledge, and vulnerabilities in a new way. I am still empowered and still in control. I think scientifically about alcohol use rather than moralistically or in an alarmist way.

I occasionally contact and hang-out with an MM friend I first met at a meeting. I still have that cherished empty whiskey bottle. I go to an out-of-state, face-to-face meeting about once a year. I still find it crucial to record my drinks, recording drinks helps me to make sure I am monitoring health and behavior risk concerns and not crossing a line into problematic alcohol use *and* it helps me to appreciate and celebrate my successes. I am proud to say MM was a huge part of my second major transition in life as I attained a master's degree, began working on a doctorate, and adopted the values of professionalism and secularism.

<u>Fiona's Story:</u> My Journey to Joy

I stopped drinking alcohol in August 2007. I went cold turkey and did not consider the idea of drinking again until March 2019. That's when I found this Moderation Management Forum. I now consider myself an occasional drinker who may have one drink at a special celebration. Giving up alcohol was the hardest thing I have ever done in my life. In 2007 I never ever thought that I would get to the place where I am at now. I am absolute proof that there is a glorious and wonderful life beyond drinking excessively. Whether you choose to abstain for a significant amount of time or successfully moderate I hope that this list helps you on your journey.

Elimination of negative actions/thoughts/emotions

1. No shame

2. No guilt

3. No embarrassment

4. No forgetfulness

5. No waking up at 4 am

6. No hangovers

7. No cravings

8. No time spent trying to remember the actions of the night before

9. No trips to shops for alcohol as I only have a drink when out for a meal

10. No time spent wondering where my next drink is coming from

Addition of positive actions/thoughts/emotions

1. Personal growth

2. Joy and peace

3. More energy

4. Waking up in the morning feeling good about myself

5. Discovering the joys of yoga

6. Discovering the joys of hula hooping

7. Self-love

8. Increase in self-worth

9. Honouring my true self

10. So much time for other activities

11. Getting to the core of who I am

12. Being completely honest with myself

13. Singing karaoke alcohol free on a cruise - twice

14. Always being present

15. The ability to observe myself—best book "*The Untethered Soul: The Journey Beyond Yourself*" by Michael A. Singer

16. Having a fantastic time at weddings being alcohol free - revealed the real experience for me

17. Better complexion

18. My desire to help other people who want to reduce their alcoholic input

Important discoveries

1.   The realization that thinking I will be happy when tipsy/drunk is an illusion.

2.   Understanding the importance that advertising places on drinking – and seeing beyond the message—it's OK not to drink or drink very little. Warnings on cigarette packets are very specific. Rather than the words "Drink Responsibly" perhaps they could also give more specific examples of the dangers of overdrinking.

3.   Drinking too much is a learned desire – it can be unlearned – listen to Brooke Castillo's podcasts 116, 117 and 118.

CHAPTER 7: THE NEXT CHAPTER

There is a saying, " You can't write a new chapter of your life if you keep re-reading your old one." The people who shared their stories in this book decided to pursue a new ending to their life story. Their stories haven't ended, they're still writing new chapters to their lives.

How about you? Have you been stuck reading the same chapter over and over, swearing every day that "today" will be the start of your new chapter? All of us were once where you are, all of us were stuck.

It's time to get unstuck. Don't keep reading other people's stories. Pick up a pen and paper. Today is the best day to start writing your own next chapter. If you don't know where to start, join one of our MM communities and we'll help.

We can't wait to read what happens next.

APPENDIX A: STEPS OF CHANGE

Guide to Moderation Management Steps of Change

Introduction

Many of the people who look into MM have already tried to get rid of their drinking problem with a big, all-at-once effort of the will – but without success. This program takes quite a different approach. The better approach is to break the change process down into a number of smaller, more manageable steps. With the step-by-step approach you gain a sense of confidence, direction and momentum as you go along. One step builds on another until at the end you have a powerful set of tools for managing your drinking behavior. And the process outlined here encourages you to customize many parts to your own situation. So you wind up with a set of control skills that really suits you as an individual, and supports a healthier, more rewarding lifestyle.

The MM Step-by-Step Approach

Here's an outline of the steps. The order in which you undertake these steps isn't critical, but it's a good idea to spend at least a little time working with each of them:

1. Start keeping a diary of your drinking, to help learn how your problems with drinking occur.

2. Look at the limits of drinking for moderate drinkers, and some of the practices and attitudes that go with moderate drinking, to get a clear picture of the moderation objective.

3. With that clear picture of what moderation looks like, consider whether moderation or abstinence seems the better objective for you. Also score your problem severity with a self-test, and consider other factors, to see whether moderation would be workable for you.

4. Make an extensive list of the problems drinking has caused you, and the benefits you expect from moderation, to strengthen your resolve.

5. Start on a period of abstinence of 30 days or more, to experience the positives of non-drinking. During this period away from alcohol you can work through some steps to help you achieve moderation.

a. Learn skills for avoiding drinking on occasions when you choose not to drink.

b. Learn skills to control drinking on occasions when you do drink.

c. Identify the key triggers that lead you to over-drink, and develop   means to neutralize those triggers.

d. Develop your own personal rules that will keep your drinking moderate.

e. Identify and start new spare-time activities that will displace drinking in your life.

6. At the end of your period of abstinence, you can start drinking again cautiously, being mindful of your limits and personal rules for drinking. Maintain a high degree of attention to your drinking during this period, including keeping a diary.

7. If and when you have slips, do a post-mortem to see what went wrong, and change your personal drinking guidelines if necessary.

Your Drinking Diary

Getting your drinking under control requires that you pay extra attention to the subject over a fair period of time. Keeping a drinking diary is a great tool for that. If you're not ready to start an abstinence period yet, you'll benefit from starting your diary right now. And you'll also keep one when you resume drinking after your abstinence period.

Here is a daily entry might include:

Occasion:
Number of drinks:
Type of drinks:
Start Time:
Stop Time:
Feeling at the time:
Identified Triggers:
Positive Activities:
Progress:

This diary will give you an objective record of your drinking behavior, and help you find the circumstances that lead to your over-drinking. Under "The Occasion" record the time of day, and where and with whom you were drinking. Your "Feelings at the Time" are likely to be important, so note those And, as discussed later, "Positive Activities" may include your drinking management tools.

What is Moderate Drinking?

Moderate drinking, first of all, means keeping drinking quantities under specific limits. Quantities are expressed in terms of customary standard-sized drinks. The standard drink here is one twelve-ounce bottle of regular (5% alcohol) beer, 5 ounces of table wine (12%), or 1.5 ounces of 80-proof liquor (40%).

The Drinking Limits are:

> For Men: No more than 14 drinks per week, and not more than 4 per occasion.
> For Women: Not more than 9 drinks per week, and not more than 3 per occasion. For Both: Do not drink on more than 3-4 days per week.

Research has shown that these limits are generally workable for persons who have learned to moderate after experiencing drinking problems. These limits are mostly the same as those set forth by the US government's

National Institute for Alcohol Abuse and Alcoholism. However, NIAAA gives a similar but slightly lower weekly limit for women of 7 drinks per week (with the same 3 per occasion), so women might want to adopt that lower weekly limit.

Note that these are upper limits rather than usual quantities. A usual quantity for a moderator is more likely to be 1-2 drinks per occasion, as a matter of individual choice. Blood alcohol levels are critical, since judgment and control are progressively lost at higher levels. Also, alcohol causes most of its physical damage at higher blood levels. MM sets 0.055% as the upper limit for blood alcohol concentration.

As well as the quantity consumed, the pace of drinking directly affects blood alcohol levels. A pace of not more than one drink per half hour helps with that. Having something to eat while drinking also helps, slowing down the uptake of alcohol into the bloodstream. The blood level also varies according to weight and sex, with heavier people getting lower levels from a given intake, and men lower levels than women. It happens that men's bodies have a higher % water, that readily dilutes alcohol, whereas women have a higher % lipids in their bodies.

You can look at a set of tables of blood alcohol levels for men and women of different weights from a given amount and pace of alcohol intake via the *moderation.org* website. Click on "Blood Alcohol Content" under the "Tools for Moderation" heading on the website's home page.

The MM upper limit of 0.055% blood alcohol compares with the legal upper limit for driving in most states of 0.080%. It's vital to obey your state's driving blood alcohol limit, and the safest practice is not to drink and drive at all.

These MM limits may strike you as stingy, but the good news is that with alcohol, less is better. The positive effects of alcohol are pretty much limited to moderate intakes in line with the MM guidelines. Drinking larger amounts, or too quickly, brings on loss of ability to fully experience what is going on, loss of control, and other negative effects. And a habit of drinking larger amounts blunts the ability to feel the positive effects of smaller amounts. You can regain that sensitivity by practicing moderation. So with moderation you can capture the benefits of drinking while avoiding the negatives.

Besides these quantitative limits, there are key attitude and lifestyle factors that go with and sustain moderate drinking behavior. Audrey Kishline, founder of Moderation Management, made up a list of these key factors back in 1994, and the list still works very well today.

The moderate drinker:

- Usually does not exceed the 0.055% blood alcohol concentration drinking limit.
- Generally has something to eat before, during, or soon after drinking.
- Usually does not drink faster than one drink per half hour.
- Usually does not drink for longer than an hour or two on any particular occasion.
- Considers an occasional drink to be a small, though enjoyable, part of life.
- Has hobbies, interests, and other ways to relax and enjoy life, that do not involve alcohol.
- Usually has friends who are moderate drinkers or non-drinkers.
- Feels comfortable with his or her use of alcohol (never drinks secretly and does not spend a lot of time thinking about drinking or planning to drink).

Your Choice of Moderation or Abstinence

A critical factor for your chance of successfully moderating is the severity of your problem. An NIAAA study comparing outcomes for persons grouped by severity showed clearly the importance of that factor. The NIAAA study followed up after three years on a group diagnosed with the most severe stage, commonly called "alcoholics," and a group at the next stage of severity, called "alcohol abuse." It turned out that 25% of the alcoholics had resolved their problem, by learning to drink at safe levels or by becoming abstinent, but more than twice as many of the abusers, or 59%, had accomplished that in the three years.

So for an objective score on the severity of your drinking problem, complete and score yourself on the "Alcohol Dependence Questionnaire" available thru the *moderation.org* website main page under the "Tools" heading. If you score 20 or above, your best bet is abstinence. With a score of 16-19, you may want to see a therapist for support in your work with drinking, including dealing with any non-alcohol issues that complicate your situation. Needless to say, you also should not continue to drink if you have physical or psychological problems that don't allow drinking.

If you're passed the severity test for trying moderation, you may also want to look at the various pros and cons of both moderation and abstinence.

Moderation of course has the advantages a) that you can still enjoy alcohol, albeit under controlled circumstances, b) that in learning moderation you will learn some self-control skills useful elsewhere in your life, and c) that you can still fit comfortably into social situations involving drinking. Negatives include a) continued exposure to a substance that has given you real problems, b) the fact that learning moderation will take a fairly significant effort over time, and c) maybe the objections of others who want you to just stop drinking. You can doubtless think of a number of other pros and cons.

Abstinence has the advantages of a) taking you completely away from the drinking problem, b) being much more simple and clear to carry out, and c) saving all the cost of alcohol. Its negatives include a) losing the pleasures of drinking, b) possible awkwardness in social situations involving drinking, and c) leaving you unprepared if you do make a slip back into drinking. Again, you can come up with others.

Most are reading this because of interest in learning moderation, so we don't expect this exercise to change many minds. But it may give you an inkling that abstinence, your fallback if moderation doesn't work down the line, is not such a bad thing after all. You'll get direct experience of abstinence if you do the recommended 30-day non-drinking period. And later when moderating you'll have some non-drinking days each week.

Building Commitment

To help build the commitment to carry through with successful change, it's helpful to go through two very personal exercises. One is to think through an extensive list of all the problems over-drinking has caused you. The other is to think through all the benefits you expect from achieving moderation.

The listing of problems from drinking is not meant to punish you – MM knows that positive motivations are stronger in the long run than negatives. But taking a quick look at the real extent of your problems with drinking at this stage will help move you forward. The trick here is to think through a list of various aspects of your life, and to see how drinking has affected each. So think about areas such as: your inner feelings, relationships with others, work issues, physical health, your finances, any legal issues, and spare time or recreation. You may be surprised to find how drinking has invaded and caused some harms in so many aspects of your life. Just recognize for once the extent of the negatives, shudder, and then move on.

The listing of benefits you expect from moderation may have some surprises on the upside. And the good news is that you will probably discover and appreciate more benefits as you go along in learning to moderate.. So again, work through a list of different aspects of your life. Under health, if your sleep isn't good when over-drinking, you'll probably get a benefit. Your appearance will doubtless improve without the stress of over-drinking. Heavier people may take off some weight without those extra calories. This list of benefits from moderation is important enough that it will pay you to put it in writing and add to it as you go along.

Your Very Own "30"

The early abstinence period in MM is simply called "The 30" by many in the program. It can be hard to get started, but there are a number of big benefits:

• You may well feel demoralized by your lack of control over drinking, and feel powerless relative to your drinking habit. When you stop drinking, suddenly you feel, and you are, back in charge.

• You get a space unclouded by alcohol to further develop your resolve for a new lifestyle, to work out your own drinking ground-rules and control strategies, and to get them firmly in mind.

• You'll enjoy the positive experiences of life without alcohol, which will help give drinking a smaller role in your mind.

• You'll learn how to say "no" to alcohol. That's important because as a moderator you won't drink on many days, and you'll refuse drinks on occasions when you've reached your limit.

• You'll see while cold sober how people really act while over-drinking. You'll take away some mental snapshots of behaviors you'd especially like to avoid.

• While drinking heavily, your tolerance for alcohol increases, so you need more for the same effect. Abstinence restores your sensitivity to alcohol, so that less is enough.

Many people who bring over-drinking under control on their own just taper down their drinking over time. But as you can see, there are very powerful advantages for an abstinence period of 30 days or more.

If you feel quite unready to start an abstinence period right now, don't force it. Keep mulling the idea over in your mind, and most likely at some point you will feel ready. Or you can start with shorter periods of non-drinking, and then go for a full month.

Learning Skills for Non-Drinking During Your "30"

As well as planning ahead for how you will manage drinking after the "30", it's a time to learn skills for the many occasions in the future when you will choose not to drink.

You may feel uneasy about drawing attention to yourself when you refuse a drink. It's best to have a few phrases ready in mind, such as: "No thanks, I'm on a diet," or "No thanks, I've got an early one tomorrow," or "No thanks, I'm the driver tonight," or just "No thanks, not tonight." You'll be pleasantly surprised how little most people are concerned. Those who do make it an issue often turn out to have drinking issues of their own. So you'll have learned that those particular people won't fit easily with your new lifestyle.

A major skill area for non-drinking is dealing with urges to drink. Techniques here include "avoidance", "confrontation" and "distraction."

"Avoidance" involves keeping away from things that give you drinking urges. Instead of having alcohol ready at hand in the house, you might want to keep it out of the house at this time, or put away or locked up in some inconvenient place. Don't spend time with heavy-drinking friends, or go to places like bars where you customarily drink. Keep busy and avoid activities during which you customarily drink, like watching sports on TV. Try to minimize stress, especially stressful situations that typically trigger heavy drinking for you. (More about triggers later). And if you're tired, thirsty, hungry, or lonely, have some rest or sustenance, or get some positive human contact as soon as possible, to head off a drinking urge.

"Confrontation" involves recognizing that you've got a drinking urge, and focusing your attention on dealing with it. The urge often seems to be saying that it won't leave you alone until you give in. The fact is, the urge will go away if you just outwait it – so mentally settle down to outwait that urge. During the waiting, you can "urge surf." That is, urges typically rise and fall like waves, and you can make a game of seeing the urge rise, crest, and then inevitably subside.

Another confrontation technique is to substitute positive for negative messages. The urge might say, for instance, that tonight is a special occasion and you can just have a drink or two and then go back to your "30." Answer the urge back with the statement: " Each time I refuse an urge I get stronger and stronger in dealing with it." Lastly, you can bring to mind your long-term objective of getting your over-drinking under control, to enjoy a healthier and more satisfying life.

"Distraction" involves having a set of activities you can get into quickly that will draw your attention away from the urge. You might, for instance, telephone a friend, go for a drive, do some housework, or any other positive activity.

Skills for Moderate Drinking

A great use for your time during your "30" is to study various techniques to help keep your drinking moderate when you do resume drinking. The list of helpful techniques is so long that you probably can't keep them all in mind. So look for a few that seem to deal best with your particular drinking issues. Get them well in mind for the time later when you'll start to drink again. As discussed later, you'll also make up a list of your personal "rules" for managing drinking, and some of these techniques may go on your "rules" list.

Control skills for drinking situations include:

- *Measuring*, since drinking guidelines are in numbers of standard-sized drinks.
- *Counting*, to keep to your guidelines.
- *Eating* helps slow the uptake of alcohol, and is an alternative pleasure.
- *The first few minutes* seem to set our style for a given drinking occasion.

- *Control thirst* by having a non-alcoholic drink before or in a drinking occasion.
- *Delaying* your first drink a bit, and/or getting to the occasion a little late.
- *Diluting* alcohol by having lower alcohol-content drinks.
- *Sipping* small amounts slowly to keep the pace of intake down.
- *Put the glass down* to avoid the automatic drinking that goes with holding a glass.
- *Time* beforehand the start of any drinks you'll have on a drinking occasion.
- *Self-Talk* during drinking about your limits, how well you are managing, etc.
- *Bring your own* non-alcoholic drinks to a party during an abs period.
- *Focus on the fun* of the occasion, not the drinking.
- *Think about tomorrow* anytime you're tempted to have more than planned.
- *Heed the "stop" signal*, that feeling that you've "had enough."

During your "30" you can rehearse the use of these control skills by thinking ahead to a typical drinking situation you might be in later. Then make up a list of the specific skills you will use in such a situation.

Your Over-Drinking Triggers

An extremely useful next step is to figure out the situations that most often lead you to over-drinking. For almost everybody, there's a definite pattern. A check-list includes timing (time of day, day of week, seasons, etc), places, activities, particular people, things directly or indirectly related to work, money issues, your physical state, relations with others (including spouse/significant other, parents, in-laws, and children), particular feeling states, and major life events. Think also about your pattern of drinking, whether your pattern is regular daily, or during certain kinds of events, or whatever. And see if your pattern is generally for fun, or generally to relieve stress or bad feelings.

After thinking all that through, you can probably spot the most important trigger or triggers for your over-drinking. So now you'll know the particular type of situation that you needto target with new behaviors. It's helpful at this point to make a written list of those key trigger situations. On the positive side, think about any other types of situations in which you usually tend to drink moderately. Thinking about those other situations can show you the behaviors and feelings you already have that go with moderate drinking.

Managing Your Triggers

Now we come to a most important step, coming up with specific ways to manage each of your important trigger situations. You should note these management strategies right on your list of triggers.

For social situations in which heavy drinking is the order of the day, at bars or with certain people, you'd best simply avoid those. And maybe there are other types of social situations where others may not be drinking too heavily but you tend to get carried away. There your rule might be to use one or more of the stronger drinking-control techniques like alternating non-alcoholic beverages, or settling into the situation for a time before your first drink.

Drinking alone is a fairly common trigger situation, because there are no social constraints on your behavior. One good technique for dealing with the "alone" times is to fill those times with activities (we'll discuss the importance of non-drinking interests shortly), so as to distract yourself. It may be necessary to set yourself a rule to just not drink alone.

Habitual drinking at a certain time of day is another common trigger. To be a moderator, per the limits, you no longer can drink every day. Keeping a calendar marked with the 3-4 days a week you may drink, will at least show you that there are oases in the desert. On days when you don't want to drink, alternative activities are a great help. If the gettinghome-from-work time is your trigger, it can help to get into some new habits, such as taking a hot shower then, or going for a walk, or going to the gym. And on days when you can drink at that certain time, really focus your thoughts on use of your chosen control techniques.

Negative feelings are more likely to lead to destructive levels of drinking than upbeat feelings. That's because we drink for mood improvement, but when we start with negative feelings the drinking may actually deepen the negatives, or not budge them much. In that case we may go on drinking just to numb our feelings, which can take a lot of booze. In general, it will be best to make it a rule not to drink when in the grip of negative emotions.

At least we have a better chance of identifying and dealing with negative emotions when our minds are clear. Recurrent depression and anxiety are feelings that may require and respond to professional treatment. For dealing with stress, there are a number of books and online resources that can give you coping strategies. For anger, the cause may be fear or frustration in not coping well. For all these, we have a better chance of identifying the problem and finding help from inner or external resources if our minds are unclouded by drinking.

If you're married and your spouse is upset about your drinking, he or she may not approve at all of your trying moderation rather than quitting. Just realize that you're in a not uncommon situation. If you can, describe the MM program to your spouse and see if you can get a little slack while you're working on it, so that the spouse doesn't go ballistic every time there's a glass in your hand. Sharing your list of triggers and strategies for dealing with them may be helpful.

Your Drinking Rules

Now that you've figured out your over-drinking triggers and how to manage them, it's time to set down a list that will be a big part of your life going forward. That's a list of your very own drinking rules. The list should be short, concise, and realistic. Including your key trigger situations is good. A limit on drinks per occasion on days when you do drink is good. Listing the couple of the control techniques on which you'll focus on drinking occasions is good.

Overall, it's what seems most important and workable to you at this point, when you're looking forward to starting drinking again after your "30." The list can be an evolving thing, modified as you find new issues coming to the fore in the future and news ways of dealing effectively with them. To help make it part of you, look it over periodically. You might even carry a folded copy with you as you start to moderate.

Non-Drinking Activities

Chances are, drinking has taken up a fair amount of your time recently. Stopping drinking for the "30," and moderate drinking on a limited number of days leaves a vacuum that needs to be filled. The great thing is, you can probably find some new or resumed activities that will give you more lasting and genuine satisfaction than all that drinking.

There may not be a lot of appealing non-drinking activities that come to mind right away. So spend a little time thinking about activities you've enjoyed at some point in the past, or ones you've simply been curious about. Let your imagination roam a bit.

Non-drinking activities that involve being with other people are particularly helpful.. Says Stanton Peele, author of *Seven Tools to Beat Addiction*: " Make sure that people you hang out with are people who look and act the way you would like to. Social imitation is the easiest form not only of flattery but of self-improvement."

Regular exercise works for a lot of people. It's good for you, and in many cases it makes you feel good. If you're quite out of shape, it may not feel good at all to start. So you may have to give it a little time, and try different types of exercise, to find something that works for you. If it doesn't make you feel good, the chances are you won't stay with it.

Things you can do at home are fine, but if a lot of your over-drinking has been at home, it's obviously good to find activities that get you out of the house. Many people find that activities involving service to others are especially rewarding.

Starting to Moderate

The "30" is a workable time-span for many people to experience life without alcohol, learn skills for non-drinking, identify over-drinking triggers and means to cope with them, list personal drinking rules, and start on new non-drinking activities. However, if it doesn't feel right to start drinking again on day 31, just keep abstinent until it does feel right.

To stay on the right track when resuming drinking, it pays to give a very high degree of attention to occasions when you drink. A tool for doing that is the diary at the end of this piece. Keeping it faithfully for at least a couple of months will give you a lot of support. It helps focus your attention on the subject. And you'll be surprised how pleased you will be to complete weeks with a clean record of moderation. Oddly enough, the thought of having to record a mistake in your diary may even keep you from taking that extra drink or other miss-step on some occasion.

Now, slips are not uncommon during this early period of practicing moderate drinking. Old habits die hard, and the new more positive habits can take some time to get well established. When you slip back into an old pattern, avoid recrimination, advises Alan Marlatt, director of the Addictive Behavior Research Center at the University of Washington. "Don't say, 'I can't do it.' People make mistakes. If you keep working at it, you'll get better over time. That's what the research shows."

The thing is to stop and figure out what went wrong and plan corrective action. If the slip happened because you broke one of your rules, maybe you need to be more alert to that particular kind of situation. If the slip uncovers some type of trigger you hadn't identified before, maybe you need a new rule to deal with that trigger.

So in the early stages of practicing moderation, accentuate the positives to yourself about the progress you're making. Don't get discouraged by a few setbacks. Giving yourself rewards for good work on moderation can be helpful, including modest things like a DVD, or a book, or eating out, or whatever.

Taking Stock for the Long Term

If you get into serious trouble with moderation, like extended over-drinking spells or breaking your rules more than you're keeping them, that's a sign to stop and take a fundamental look at what's going on. It may help to start a new abstinence period. During this abs period you can re-work the steps, looking especially at your triggers and rules. If you don't see a way to get back on the track to moderation, maybe you need to see a therapist who deals with addiction problems for more support.

In the long term, many in MM find it useful to do an annual repeat "30," or at least an abs period of more than a couple of days. Just getting alcohol completely out of your life for awhile can reinforce your self-control. And it can be a very satisfying time of moving through the changes in circumstances and mood that life brings, completely free of the effects of drinking.

If you continue to experience serious problems in trying to moderate, it's likely that moderation just isn't for you at this time. Altogether, around 1/3 of the people who get significantly involved with MM eventually find that abstinence is their best resolution. Most of those people find that MM has been helpful in giving them a firm indication of the right resolution for their drinking problem.

MM Resources for Support

Background on MM

On the moderation.org (http://moderation.org/) home page, under the "About MM" heading there is material on the background and philosophy of MM, supportive "Research," and a large collection of member comments on a variety of topics under the "FAQ" heading.

Group Support

MM Closed Facebook Group (https://www.facebook.com/groups/462485394489953/)

MM Forum (https://forum.moderation.org/forum)

MM Listserv (http://www.moderation.org/online/mmlist_welcome.ht ml)

<u>MM Meetings</u>
(http://www.moderation.org/meetings/index.html)

Individual Therapist Support

<u>Find a Moderation-Friendly Therapist</u>.
(http://members.moderation.org/)

Interactive Programs

Checkup and Choices for MM
(https://checkupandchoices.com/mm/#utm_source=MM
&utm_medium=banner&utm_campaign=Jan_29_2019_
update&utm_content=side%20banner):

If you already know you want to make changes in your life and want help, the Choices Program offers exercises and tools to help you moderate or quit. You will have access to all of the Choices Program modules and you decide which module(s) you want to do based on your personal needs and goals: Moderate Alcohol, Abstain Alcohol, Abstain Marijuana, Abstain Opioids and Abstain Stimulants.

Medication Assisted Moderation:

RIA Health (https://riahealth.com/moderation-management/): RIA health combines telemedicine, medication, coaching and a breathalyzer tracking app in an at-home program that helps people reduce their drinking or quit completely. *My coach made the difference. She helped me through rough spots, gave motivation, and helped come up with ideas. Following the app twice a day was the other key.*

Further Written Steps of Change Material

For further reading, on the *moderation.org* home page check the "Suggested Reading List" under "Tools."

The *"Responsible Drinking"* (https://www.amazon.com/Responsible-Drinking-Moderation-Management-Approach/dp/1572242949) book by Rotgers et al lays out the MM program at length.

"Changing for Good" (https://www.amazon.com/Changing-Good-Revolutionary-Overcoming-Positively/dp/038072572X/) by James O. Prochaska

"Controlling Your Drinking"
(https://www.amazon.com/Controlling-Your-Drinking-Second-Moderation-ebook/dp/B00DG1H8W8) by Miller & Munoz is particularly strong on discussing alternative activities to drinking.

"Rethinking Drinking"
(*https://www.rethinkingdrinking.niaaa.nih.gov/*) by the US government's National Institute for Alcohol Abuse and Alcoholism is a moderation guide similar to this , downloadable free at www.niaaa.nih.gov.

Support for Abstinence

- Alcoholics Anonymous (https://www.aa.org/). Has the longest track record and the largest number of local face-to-face meetings. Just look in the phone book.

- MMAbsers: Support for MM members who choose abstinence for any period of time. Welcomes members of other abstinence-based programs.

- o Life Ring Secular Recovery (https://www.lifering.org/) An organization that share practical experiences and support.

- o SMART Recovery (https://www.smartrecovery.org/). Based on modern psychology; deals with a variety of addictions; groups led by trained individuals.

- o Women for Sobriety (https://womenforsobriety.org/). For the special needs of women, emphasizing individual competence and responsibility. www.womenforsobriety.org.

APPENDIX B:
TOOLBOX

TOOLS

1. Delay Tool: Start drinking one hour later.

2. NA-N-Between Tool: One NA drink between each alcoholic drink

3. Stop 1 hour earlier

4. Make-believe Moderate Companion: Ask yourself what your   moderate drinking companion would do, then do that.

5. Abstain for 1 day: One day has so much power in it.

6. Drink 1 drink for the day: Just got have a drink? Have "A" drink.

7. Decrease your drinks by 1: Less is less

8. TTYD Tool: Talk to your drink. When you're about to grab that drink that is going to put you over your limit, ask it, "What's in it for me if I drink you?" Then ask it,

"What's in it for me, if I don't drink you."

9. Play The Movie To The End Tool: What will happen if you drink that next drink? How will it change tomorrow? Next week? Next month? Do another reversal and play the movie to the end if you don't drink that drink.

10. The Self-Mark-up Tool: Today, you are going to raise the value on yourself by showing the rest of the world that you are a top-of-the-line item. We tend to treat the items that we value, the ones we spend more time or money on, with more care. So today, spend a little more time on your make-up or your hair. Spritz on the cologne. Iron your shirt or put on your favorite outfit. Treat yourself to a pedicure or a massage. Show the world and yourself that what's on the inside is worth the price. Because....YOU are!

11. Surfboard Tool: Surf the Urge. Sometimes, especially in the beginning, you can't avoid those monster waves of urges, you've got to learn to surf them. Just like a wave builds in intensity and height, so do urges, but if you can ride it out until it crests, it quickly loses its intensity

12. Walk away from the drink tool: Leave your drink on the table while you mingle at a party or while you tuck

your kids into bed. Give yourself a break.

13. The Trigger Transformer: Transform a trigger by reacting in a new way that doesn't include drinking.

14. The Buddy-Up Tool: Find someone who has the same goal as you and Buddy-Up to help both of you achieve success.

15. Hire Some Help Tool: Tell one person you care about and trust that you are decreasing your drinking and you need their help. Ask them to be there when you feel yourself weakening, to answer the phone, to take you for a walk and talk, to slap you on the back when you turn down that drink another friend is trying to tempt you with. You will be so surprised how quickly they will jump to your defense when others try to sway you to revert back to your ways. People love to be needed. (Not a good idea to choose your favorite drinking buddy for this role.).

16. Take The Lead Tool: We are more likely to succeed at reaching our goals if we empower ourselves by taking the lead and asking others to follow us. We have taken the responsibility of setting an example for others. More pressure? Sure. But tons more incentive to succeed, too.

We are more apt to do for others what we haven't been able to do for ourselves.

17. The AF Hangover Tool: The instructions for using this tool include: Do not drink the night before; Sleep as late as you want; Stay in your pajamas, or onesie, or favorite pair of sweats all day; Do not comb hair, brushing teeth is optional; Pancakes with lots of butter and syrup for breakfast; Keep the shades pulled down; Pick out a season of something to binge watch;

Do not feel one twinge of guilt!

We all need days like this sometimes, even if we're sober (At MM, successful moderation is sobriety, too.). Sometimes we get so busy staying busy so we don't drink, we need to slow down and feel the benefits of being lazy and slothlike. The AF Hangover Tool can be a great incentive to not drink the night before.

18. Yet Obliterator Tool: The next time you find yourself using a "Yet" as a reason to drink more than you know you should, obliterate that thought. ~~I haven't gotten a DUI yet. I've never lost a job, yet.~~ By doing this, you not only remove a stumbling block from reaching your goal, you obliterate your chance of every achieving one of those

cataclysmic "Yets" that could forever change your life in a negative way.

19. The GPS Tool: Let's map our journey out. Where do we want to go tonight, how are we going to get there, what do we need to pack to take with us, do we have enough gas in the tank? Where do we want to be at the end of the week, what kind of obstacles are going to be in the way and how do we get around them? A month? 3 months? A year? We may not reach our intended destinations by these mileposts, but we need to stop once in a while and take stock of where we are. Are we still on the road? Have we gotten stuck? What do we need to get unstuck? Backed up? Do we need a push from our fellow travelers? Is it time to head off in a new direction? Without our GPS tool, it's easy to get lost and keep going in circles.

20. The Toothbrush Tool: That's right, your simple toothbrush, doesn't just fight cavities, it fights cravings by getting that lingering taste out of your mouth so your brain doesn't keep expecting more. Brushing your teeth at night, sends a signal to the brain that you are done imbibing, whether that be of sugar or wine or whatever your poison-have you ever drank a glass of wine right after brushing your teeth? Blech!

21. MIMD (Make It More Difficult) Tool; This is an adaptable tool and can be adapted to any circumstance. Some of you are already using it by not keeping alcohol in your house and only buying the amount you're going to drink that day or opening the bottle and pouring the booze out until you only have the amount you intend to drink. Some of us who co-habitate with fellow drinkers might find dumping all the alcohol meets with grave disapproval but you can still find ways to make access for you more difficult. Tell your co-habitee they need to keep their booze under lock and key for a while. Yes, we know how persuasive we can be when we decide to break our promise to ourselves and decide to grant ourselves that "one more drink" wish but having to ask someone else if you can have it, makes it much more difficult.

22. The Contract: Write down what you want to achieve, how much less you promise to drink. Make the contact for a day, a week, a month and a year. Get a calendar and write down your promise for each day and put that calendar where you and others can see it. Did you know if we put that promise down on paper, we're less likely to break it? If we get other people involved and make a contract with them to change our behavior, it strengthens the contract even more.

23. The Reward Tool: It's time to treat yourself. Buy those shoes you've been eyeing or that set of golf clubs or treat yourself to your favorite activity. Of course, you could just give yourself a pat on the back if that's all you need to keep yourself from the booze, but we think YOU deserve more than that! You're a Super Hero! When we drink, we get a reward, right? We get that warm fuzzy feeling, that sense of enhanced community with friends, that "I love you, I really do!" gushiness, our devil-may-care sense of fun. No wonder it's so hard to reduce our drinking, it's like putting all our toys back in the toy box and locking it and throwing away the key. That's why it is imperative to reinforce our choice of better habits with a reward, otherwise we're going to go looking for that key to our toybox.

24. The "I Can" Tool: The fact is, we can do anything we want. It may suck. It may be hard. It may scare the crap out of us. It may take learning a new skill or getting help, but we can do it. Whenever we hear ourselves telling ourselves, "I can't get through this without drinking, we need to counter that with, "I can get through without drinking, it's going to be hard but I can get through it.

25. The Do Something Nice For Someone Else Tool: Today, do one thing for someone else. It can be a stranger on a continent on the other side of the world or it can be someone sitting next to you right now. It can cost money, or it can cost time. It may not make a noticeable change in our drinking habits, but it will remind us that we are so much more than our problem, we are worth fighting for.

26. The Almighty Plan Tool: How many times have we gone into an evening, or a weekend, or a wedding or a pub and simply told ourselves, "I'm just going to drink less" only to wake up the next morning with our oh-so-familiar companions: aching head, sour belly and defeated soul? We failed to plan and, hence, planned to fail. Don't just plan in your head, get a pencil and paper and write it down, maybe include an inspirational quote or a list of reasons not to stray from your plan, tuck it in your pocket, then, WORK YOUR PLAN.

27. The Assertive aka Put Yourself First Tool: I can't describe this tool any better than Jame's Prochaska does in his book, "Changing for Good." According to Dr. Prochaska, you have certain rights, amongst them, the right to put your well-being and happiness first, the right to have your desires to change respected and the right to be heard. In the beginning, many of us scramble together

half-true or fabricated excuses to explain to others why we're not drinking, but we show a true intention to change when we let others know, brooking no argument, that we are "changing for good," the good of ourselves and we refuse to make excuses.

28. The Divorce Tool: Perform a divorce between something you automatically drink while doing. Grab a beer the minute you walk in the door from work? Grab a nutritional drink to rejuvenate yourself instead. Can't cook without a glass of wine dangling from your hand? Grab some water instead and save the wine for the meal. Drink until you go to bed, keep that last drink in the bottle or box and brew up some Sleepy Time Tea instead. Break ups are hard but necessary when the relationship becomes toxic.

29. Accountability: Remember accountability is one of the most powerful tools, when you declare publicly, or to even one other person, that you are going to do something, you are much more likely to accomplish what you said you would.

30. Hope! Don't lose it. If you misplace your own, borrow it from someone else until you find it again.

31. Don't Give Up Tool: The only failure comes from giving up. You can take a break, you can regroup, you can try another path or join another group, but as long as you don't give up, you will not fail.

OTHER MODERATION MANAGEMENT PUBLICATIONS:

Dryuary 2019 Collection

(https://www.amazon.com/gp/product/B07N88ZYRP)

If you are currently in the process of completing a 30-Day Abstinence period, are contemplating a future 30-Day Abstinence Period, or gearing up for the upcoming **Dryuary 2020_** campaign, the Dryuary 2019 Collection is a great source of daily inspiration and expert advice. Contributors include: Annie Grace; Rachel Hart; Dr. Amy Johnson; Jackie Elliot; Dr. Adi Jaffe; Clare Pooley; Jason Garner; Lotta Dann and past Dryuary participants who want to share their stories.

Other Books by Mary Reid:

Neighbor Kary May's Handbook To Happily Drinking Less Or Not Drinking At All, Quite Happily: With The Help Of The Online Recovery Community

(https://www.amazon.com/dp/B01LWICGL6)

Part memoir, part self-help book, Kary May (aka Mary Reid) takes us on a sometimes tearful, often joyful, and occasionally "Sister Pencil Thin Mustache of the Order of the Holy Wooden Ruler" inspired bossy chronical of her recovery with the support of the MM community.

"I thoroughly enjoyed this book because it weaves Kary May's story within many resources to help someone quit drinking or drink less. I can appreciate and enjoyed Kary May's straight forward and down to earth voice in telling her story as it relates to the paths she took, and those she did not. I learned a lot about various approaches and communities of people in the sober world, some of which I did not know before. This book opened my mind a bit more about different viewpoints, and therefore this book is a wonderful resource in which I will refer to often."

BEFORE YOU GO:

We hope that this book has encouraged you to make positive changes in your life, or to continue the journey you have already begun. If you are not part of the MM community, we look forward to getting to know you. Please visit Moderation.org (http://moderation.org/) to join one of our communities or just say, "Hi!"

If you're lost in the dark, email (mm@moderation.org) us a message with "Help" in the subject line, we have flashlights and lots of batteries and chocolate because chocolate is necessary for survival. And ice cream...with chocolate sauce. Oh, and shoulders, lots of sometimes soggy shoulders to lean or cry on. We only ask that you loan us your shoulder when we need to lean or cry. None of us need to be lost and alone in the dark any longer.

Please take a few minutes to leave a review and tell us what you thought of this book and if it has made a difference in your life, what you think is really important to us.

To stay informed about new events, publications and resources at MM, sign up to receive our newsletter by sending an email to whatsnew@moderation.org.

Just one more thing, you can help us help more people write their success story by donating to MM at http://moderation.org/donate.html. Your donation helps us to continue to offer support to all who need it at no cost to them.

Made in the USA
Las Vegas, NV
16 February 2022

44015072R00148